Over 70 MURDER MYSTERY CROSSWORDS

SIMON
MELHUISH

BARNES
&NOBLE

NEW YORK

Originally published as *Mad Moose's Mega Murder Mystery Crosswords.*
© 2001 by Mad Moose Press

This edition published exclusively by Barnes & Noble Publishing
by arrangement with Lagoon Trading Company Limited.

2006 Barnes & Noble Publishing

ISBN-13: 978-0-7607-8064-0
ISBN-10: 0-7607-8064-1

Printed and bound in the United States of America

3 5 7 9 10 8 6 4 2

Here is a collection of Murder Mystery Crosswords for you to tackle. In each puzzle a calamitous murder has taken place. Superintendent U. Sless is called out to investigate each murder but always gets waylaid for some reason and you, his faithful assistant, end up having to work it out yourself. Read the statements from three witnesses. These will help you to solve the clues in the crossword. When you have completed the crossword unscramble the letters in the shaded squares and the murderer and the murder weapon will be revealed.

Paper Chase

Murder most foul has been committed at Tover Towers. The body of Dusty Binns, journalist, has been found brutally battered in the Penthouse Suite. Superintendent U. Sless has been dispatched to investigate, but unfortunately took the elevator to the basement and has become hopelessly lost, so it is up to you to catch the culprit.

LORD TOVER

"This is an outrage!" spluttered Lord Tover, newspaper magnate, pushing his pipe into his trouser pocket. "However, I can't say I'm sorry he's gone, he was a complete imbecile and couldn't do anything right." In that case, had he decided to take matters into his own hands? "Certainly not!" he exclaimed, looking out the skyscraper window. "I think it was Ina, my secretary. Dusty always put white sugar in her coffee and she likes demerara. It finally got under her skin and she snapped."

INA TWIST

"That's ridiculous," snorted Ina. "I'm not going to get insomnia, or commit murder over something as trivial as that. Nobody idolized Dusty, but they liked him. He was a good reporter and he wrote some excellent material, sometimes the words flowed out like lava and he always had a ready anecdote." In that case, who had performed the dastardly deed? "Orson was always winding him up," she replied with a delicate shudder, "teasing him about his aspiration to be a jockey, twirling an imaginary lariat and making fun of his pony, Luke. Orson's your culprit."

ORSON RAILLES

"I've never been so insulted in my life," snarled Orson. "Sure I used to tease him, but amidst it all, we got on fine and worked well together." So, who did he think killed Dusty? "I reckon Lord Tover did," replied Orson. "He's made no secret of the fact he couldn't stand him. And when Dusty broke his favorite pen, with which he did perfect italic writing, that was the final straw!"

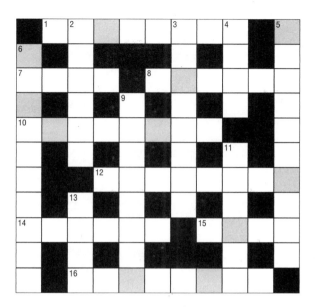

ACROSS

1 Dusty wrote this, excellently (8)
7 Get under this, as Dusty did to Ina (4)
8 The type of horse rider Dusty wanted to be (6)
10 Sleeplessness—not Ina's problem (8)
12 The right type of sugar (8)
14 Lord Tover's perfect writing style (6)
15 Shouldn't be pushed into pockets when lit (4)
16 Always ready with a good one (8)

DOWN

2 In the middle of all this (6)
3 Nobody looked up to Dusty (8)
4 Pony named after a Gospel writer (4)
5 Lots of windows to look out of in this building (10)
6 Hope—the sort Dusty had (10)
9 Was the victim this kind of idiot (8)
11 Orson liked twirling an imaginary lasso (6)
13 Flowing out—like this (4)

2

School for Scandal

The body of Noah Braines, problem pupil at Clever Clogs High School, has been found behind the stage in the school hall. Superintendent U. Sless, who has a particular dislike of schools, has sent you to conduct the investigation instead.

TERRY FYDE

"An obnoxious pest has been laid to rest!" chortled Terry. "We will be celebrating in the staff room today!" Did he have any ideas about the killer? "Miss Treat was a favorite victim of his. Yesterday he smeared Vaseline on the doorknob of the toilets and the poor lady couldn't get out! Then he stood outside her villa last night chanting lewd slogans while she was trying to watch the news, which she loves for its morbidity! Hanging offense that I should imagine! The last straw was kicking her cat, Diaz!"

MISS TREAT

"Stuff and nonsense!" exclaimed Miss Treat. "I didn't kill the little horror!" Did she know who did? "There is a large shoal who would have liked to but I rather suspect it was Dee. She has been a widow for only three months and Noah kept telling everyone she poisoned her husband! He walked past her yesterday and gave her a nudge and she spilled her beaker of juice all over her swiss roll and down the front of her orlon skirt and then he had the nerve to blame a stray zephyr wafting past!"

DEE VINE

"Unfortunately, no, I didn't do it!" asserted Dee. "But I would have liked to sunder him!" Did she have any clues as to who did? "I think it was Terry. Noah was a big bully and got poor Terry in a nelson yesterday. As Terry tried to break free, Noah started to spar with him and made his nose bleed. It looked like the final hours at the Alamo! Then Noah began to tramp up and down and exploded a paper bag of flour all over everything. The noise and mess was terrible—it looked and sounded like an H-bomb going off!"

ACROSS

1 This was smeared on (8)
7 The skirt material (5)
8 Dee had been one for only three months (5)
9 The juice was in this container (6)
10 What Miss Treat was watching (4)
12 The cat's name (4)
14 A stray breeze wafting past (6)
17 Noah did this, up and down (5)
18 Like a large group who would have liked to have done it (5)
19 What the greasy substance was smeared on (8)

DOWN

1 Miss Treat's house (5)
2 Dee would have like to split Noah apart (6)
3 Noah chanted dirty slogans (4)
4 ...and what he did to cause the juice to spill (5)
5 Why Miss Treat loved the news (9)
6 The juice was spilt on this food (5, 4)
11 A wrestling hold used (6)
13 A resemblance to this American battle (5)
15 It looked and sounded like this going off (1-4)
16 Noah started to fight with Terry and made his nose bleed (4)

3

Kitchen Calamity

The brutally murdered body of Fred Uffer has been found in the shared kitchen of a block of apartments in Lower Slaughter. As Superintendent U. Sless has inadvertently gone to the bathroom by mistake, it is up to you to apprehend the culprit.

COLLEEN HOME

"Poor old Fred!" exclaimed Colleen. "We are going to miss him around here." Any idea who killed him? "I wouldn't put it past Erin—the two of them were a duet of animosity at times. He was always off overseas, he spent Christmas in Bern, and Easter in France, and came back with loads of Breton food and drink. The cheese was great, the only trouble is he left it out and the mice moved in. She was livid and the poor bloke had to grovel for weeks before she would speak to him again!"

ERIN DOORS

"Utter nonsense!" stated Erin. "That woman doesn't know what she's on about." Did she know who had killed Fred? "Of course, that ridiculous Lou. Fred had an agar culture in the fridge and the silly lady touched it with her finger, and then the end of her nose, which then developed a septic boil! That will teach her not to meddle! She went into a sulk and wouldn't speak to him. When she saw the movie *Carrie* was on TV she was very curt with him and was vehement that the universe would be a better place without him!"

LOU SOME

"It wasn't me!" cried Lou. "I'm not a murderer!" Who is then? "Colleen is my guess. She finds it hard to relate to anyone and her continual use of metaphor is very annoying. She had made a mock-up of some garden she is designing and Fred unfortunately caught the table with his feet and the whole lot rolled on to the floor. I have never seen anyone so furious as she was!"

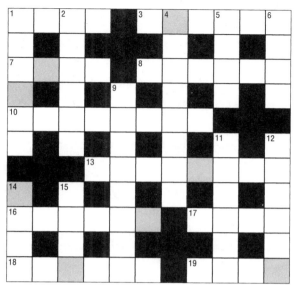

ACROSS

1 These animals moved in (4)
3 The whole lot did what on to the floor (6)
7 Lou was very this with Fred (4)
8 That will teach Lou not to do this (6)
10 Where would be a better place without Fred (8)
13 Colleen's continual use of what is very annoying (8)
16 Fred had to do what to Erin for weeks (6)
17 What part of Fred caught the table (4)
18 Colleen finds it hard to do this with anyone (6)
19 Christmas was spent where (4)

DOWN

1 Colleen made this kind of model of a garden she was designing (4-2)
2 The film Lou wanted to watch (6)
4 Fred was always off where (8)
5 The silly what touched it with her finger (4)
6 They were this kind of twosome of animosity (4)
9 Lou was this way about the world being better without Fred (8)
11 This food was great (6)
12 And what its origin was (6)
14 What sort of culture was in the fridge (4)
15 And what it caused on Lou's nose (4)

Medic Mayhem

There's trouble at the Last Chance Clinic. Doctor Martin Ett, director, has been found brutally murdered by the front doors. Superintendent U. Sless is scared of hospitals, so has asked you, his trusty assistant, to investigate this crime.

PHIL BETTER

"I'm the head doctor here," announced Phil, striding forward across the pavement. "Terrible news about Martin; since he became a director, things have vastly improved. He's certainly been very impressed with some of my ideas. And he shows tremendous equity in his dealings with patients and staff alike." Did he have any idea who the killer was? "It must have been that worn-out sawbones, Peter. Ever since the outbreak of bubonic plague among the convention of archaeologists who recently returned from the Inca excavations, he's been ranting at Martin for not having isolated them immediately."

PETER DOWT

"I was upset with Martin—my pet rabbit, Eden, died in the laboratory during the plague," responded Peter. "I loved that rabbit, I smuggled her into the country after my holiday in Faro last year. But I didn't kill Martin." If he didn't, who did? "Eliza must have done it—she's got acrophobia and he made her work on the top floor. She's gone to pieces and all detail has gone out of her work. He was going to banish her altogether—send her back to Arkansas, where she comes from!"

ELIZA PAYNE

"That's pathetic," cried Eliza, "I was planning on giving up medicine and returning home anyway. I was going to assemble everyone today and break the news to them!" When asked who might have attacked Martin, she frowned. "I do believe it was Phil. He's been having arguments with Martin whose outlook wasn't very modern. The crux of the matter is, Phil murdered Martin so that he could be in complete charge!"

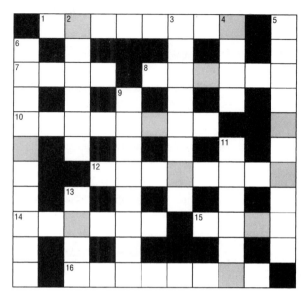

4

ACROSS

1 Give up this career—like Eliza (8)
7 It's the nub of it all (4)
8 Not a very up-to-date outlook, unlike Martin's (6)
10 Sudden occurrence of the plague (8)
12 Phil strode across this (8)
14 Martin was going to oust Eliza (6)
15 Where Peter's pet came from (4)
16 Eliza was planning to gather everyone together (8)

DOWN

2 Martin's sort of fairness (6)
3 What the archaeologists should have been immediately (8)
4 A strange name for a rabbit, perhaps (4)
5 Our sick diggers were a group of this type (10)
6 No good working up high with this (10)
9 Eliza's home state (8)
11 Attention to this is missing from Eliza's work (6)
13 What sort of excavations had the archaeologists come from (4)

Hack a Havoc

The body of Lee Thurboot has been found brutally murdered in a stall at the Tack 'n' Hack Stables. As Superintendent U. Sless has bad memories of being chased by a Shetland pony, it is up to you to solve the crime.

FRANK MANNER

"Lee was a bit of a despot, I have to admit!" stated Frank. "He certainly kept his finger on the pulse. And he always demanded his pound of flesh." Any idea whodunit? "Jose is a bit of a bad boy, and Lee used to come down rather heavy at times. Jose comes from Mexico but fancies himself a bit of a gaucho. Great fan of the jockey Lester Piggott and also once sold tickets at Aintree Racecourse. Lee had a complaint from the police that Jose was riding one of the horses round the roller skating rink. Lee was furious and said he would take great delight in having his visa revoked."

JOSE RYDER

"Si, I make the boss angry!" exclaimed Jose. "But I do not kill him." Any guess about who did? "Doug was another who always make the boss angry. He had some morello cherry jam sandwiches which he do not like, so he pushed them down the chimney flue of the incinerator which blocked it. Smoke everywhere. Lee thinks stables are going to burn. He tried to accost Doug and threatened to fire him."

DOUG TUCKER

"I didn't do it, no matter what that little earwig says," sneered Doug. "He is just a gust of hot air." Did he have any clues about the culprit? "Behind Frank's sedate exterior is a monster trying to take over the stables. He has tried to hamstring Lee at every turn. He arrives late for work most days. He had to sign for a delivery of feed the other day and didn't bother checking the quality—it was all worm-ridden. Lee had just about had enough and tried to deflate that bumptious fool by telling him it was about time he moved on. I don't think Frank liked that one little bit!"

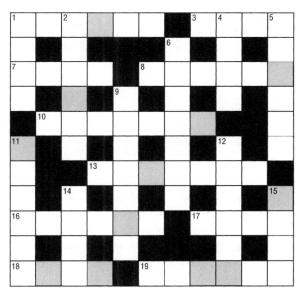

5

ACROSS

1 Frank had this kind of exterior (6)
3 What the sandwiches blocked (4)
7 Doug thinks Jose is a what of hot air (4)
8 Jose was a fan of Piggot, this famous jockey (6)
10 What type of cherry jam (7)
13 Where Jose used to sell tickets (7)
16 He fancied himself as a bit of a South American cowboy (6)
17 What Lee threatened to do to Doug (4)
18 The roller skating area that Jose was riding one of the horses around (4)
19 Lee tried to confront Doug (6)

DOWN

1 Frank had to do this for a delivery of feed (4)
2 Lee was this kind of a tyrant (6)
4 Frank arrives this most days (4)
5 Doug called Jose a little insect (6)
6 Lee tried to humiliate the bumptious fool (7)
9 Lee would have had great pleasure in revoking Jose's visa (7)
11 Digit he kept on the pulse (6)
12 Country Jose comes from (6)
14 Lee thought the stables were going to do this (4)
15 Lee held his **11D** on the pulse (4)

6

Gory Gardening

The brutally murdered body of Tom Thrum has been found in the tool shed at Little Bicker Acres. As Superintendent U. Sless is admiring the runner beans, it is up to you to solve the crime.

DICK WITLESS

"He finally got his comeuppance, then!" stated Dick. "He was going senile, poor old fool." Any idea who killed him? "He had a fight with Harry on the weekend—flung a nail carton at him which made a gash on his forehead. Harry's wife, Nora put some aloe vera lotion on it which seems to have halted any infection but there will be a scar. The secretary was going to serve a writ on Tom, then throw him out, but it looks like Harry jumped the gun!"

HARRY UPP

"It wasn't me!" exclaimed Harry. "But I shan't weep with sorrow!" Did he know who it was? "Sol is usually quite genial but wasn't averse to arguing with Tom. Sol likes to potter around and unearths some interesting finds. He dug up an old Tyrian coin last week and Tom was going through all the archives to try to prove he had a claim on it, as it was on his boundary. Tom got so heated up he threw a turnip at Sol, who fell and banged his head on the pier!"

SOL ANGRY

"Ha, it wasn't me!" roared Sol. "And amen to that!" Who was it then? "Dick is a bit of a firebrand at times. Tom had a tern with a broken wing he'd been nursing. When it was healed, the old fool released it here and it immediately swooped down and started gulping down the orfe in Dick's pond. He tried to overtake it but it kind of went hard astern and headed off towards the coast. Dick was heard to say he was going to stop Tom's shenanigans once and for all!"

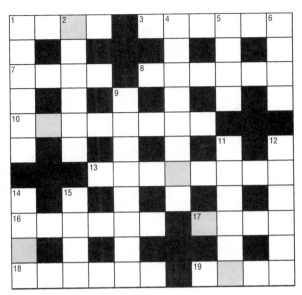

ACROSS

1 What did Harry have on his forehead (4)

3 What Tom threw at Sol (6)

7 Harry's wife (4)

8 Dick thought Tom was losing his memory (6)

10 The soothing lotion (4, 4)

13 Tom was going through all the old records looking to prove his claim (8)

16 The coin dug up (6)

17 The type of fish in Dick's pond (4)

18 Sol likes to mosey around (6)

19 Bird with the broken wing (4)

DOWN

1 Sol was usually quite friendly (6)

2 Harry shan't weep with sadness (6)

4 Sol does this with some interesting finds (8)

5 What was in the carton flung at Harry (4)

6 What Sol banged his head on (4)

9 Dick tried to do this to the bird (8)

11 Sol wasn't against the odd row (6)

12 The bird kind of went hard in what direction (6)

14 Dick was going to end Tom's shenanigans (4)

15 The secretary was going to serve Tom with this legal document (4)

The Graceful Dead

Grace Fooly, member of the exclusive Sunny Hills Ladies Health Club, has been found brutally murdered in the sauna. Superintendent U. Sless has accidentally driven his car into the new outdoor swimming pool, so it is up to you, his trusted assistant, to find the culprit.

ELLIE GHANT

"I can't believe it," wept Ellie. "Who would want to kill Grace, such a lovely lady, we've been friends for years." Has she any idea at all who could have murdered Grace? "Lena, the instructor, disliked her intensely. When she gave Grace a body wrap the other day, she wouldn't permit her to keep her nicotine patch on. Grace was so furious she threw a china figurine at Lena, which unfortunately missed!"

LENA ANSLEM

"That woman is a fool," scoffed Lena, "I value my job too much to assault the clients—even if they deserve it!" So who could possibly have done it? "I think it was Winnie, the manageress," she glanced around furtively. " Since Grace returned from vacationing in Piedmont, she hasn't been very sensible—kicked up a fuss about a missing apostrophe in our newsletter and told Winnie a Palm Court-style dining room would uplift the establishment! She always has her edam and pear salad by the swimming pool! Winnie was at the end of her tether with Grace's tantrums—and Winnie mad is not a pretty sight!"

WINNIE SOMME

"So, that's what she thinks of me, is it?" snapped Winnie. "She certainly won't be employed here after today! I've never been so insulted in my life, to be accused of killing someone!" If she didn't, who did? "Ellie, of course," responded Winnie. "She's been jealous of Grace for years. Money, looks, you name it, Grace has it and Ellie hasn't. They fell out over their hairdresser and Grace spitefully told her she should be incarcerated on an island in the middle of the Severn River from where she couldn't escape. Ellie wasn't able to string a coherent sentence together, she was so tongue-tied with rage and humiliation. If there hadn't been a crowd of spectators, I reckon Ellie would have finished her off there and then!"

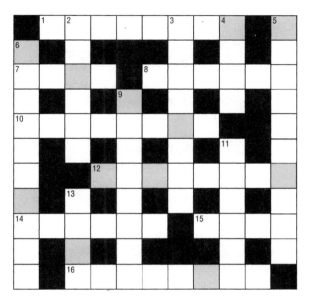

ACROSS

1 China ornament that missed, unfortunately (8)
7 This court would uplift the establishment (4)
8 Ellie wouldn't be able to get away from the **2D** (6)
10 Grace wasn't this when she came back from holiday (8)
12 A sentence that made sense (8)
14 Wouldn't allow her (6)
15 A tasty fruit accompaniment with the salad (4)
16 Where Grace spent her vacation (8)

DOWN

2 A place in the middle of the river (6)
3 Winnie was offended, to be accused of murder (8)
4 Cheese in the salad (4)
5 If there hadn't been this around, Ellie would have finished her off, there and then (10)
6 Caused a fuss about missing this punctuation mark (10)
9 Grace wasn't allowed to keep this patch on (8)
11 The name of the river (6)
13 What Grace had around her body (4)

8

Counted Out!

The battered body of Count Koynz has been found at the exclusive Well-Heeled Club.
Superintendent U. Sless is busy arguing the cost of valet service
so it is once again up to you to solve the murder.

BENNY FISCHERY

"Bad show," exclaimed Benny. "It'll be odd not watching the Count adding up his dinar over the silver service in the dining room." Did he have any ideas who might have done it? "It wouldn't amaze me to hear it was Lester—he's a thug, you know. I don't like to dwell on it but I've heard disturbing news of him from our consulate in New Zealand. Lester was doing trade in illegally exporting Maori artifacts! The Count was a retired diplomat, but kept his finger on the pulse of international affairs and taxed him with it!"

LESTER PAYE

"Don't pay any attention to that obese fool," said Lester. "He's a bit long in the tooth and an intolerable pest with his ferreting around in other's business!" Did he have any clues then? "Yes, Harry—there's been rumors about him! The Count actually saw him dressed in women's lingerie at London's Euston Station and would tease him about it. I think Harry was worried it might become common knowledge!"

HARRY STOCRAT

"What a lot of nonsense," asserted Harry as his shoulders gave a delicate judder. "I did not do it!" Any ideas who did then? "Indeed, yes. Benny is your man! For our centenary, the Count offered to have his chef prepare a traditional dish of lamb, rolled in oats, as our main course. Benny was adamant that most members would prefer something plainer! More than just a tinge of animosity there—they came to blows in the billiards room!"

ACROSS

1 The Count was a retired one (8)
7 Benny was a fat fool (5)
8 The Count would do this to Harry (5)
9 The dining room service (6)
10 Benny was an intolerable nuisance (4)
12 The meat in the traditional dish (4)
14 The London station where Harry was seen (6)
17 Benny was a bit long in the molar (5)
18 The currency the Count liked adding up (5)
19 What type of women's clothing did Harry like wearing (8)

DOWN

1 Benny doesn't like to linger on the disturbing news (5)
2 Most members would like their food plainer (6)
3 Meat dish was rolled in what (4)
4 It wouldn't what Benny to hear it was Lester (5)
5 News from our where in New Zealand (9)
6 Celebration of a 100 years (9)
11 Harry gave a delicate shake (6)
13 What sort of artifacts were being illegally exported (5)
15 There was more than just a bit of animosity (5)
16 Benny thought Lester was a ruffian (4)

Catch of the Day

The body of local fisherman, Mike Netts, has been found under an upturned boat on the shore at Shingle Bay. Superintendent U. Sless cannot abide the smell of fish so it is up to you to investigate the killing.

BARNACLE BILL

"Ahoy, there," greeted Bill. "This is like watching Columbo on TV!" Did he have any clues? "Well, now, I saw Mike and Gary throwing buckets at each other the other day. Gary holds a grudge when thwarted. He likes to adhere to the same old fishing grounds but Mike reckoned they should move around a bit—their weekly wage had dropped and his wife would rebuke him for not earning enough. She once hit him over the head with a skillet. Gary told him to put a bit of starch in his backbone and stand up to her. Times are lean and those two men had reached a parting of the ways!"

GARY GOPHER

"Rubbish," snorted Gary. "I didn't kill my best friend—not over something so trivial." So who did then? "Jack's been a bit antisocial lately. He's a feisty guy mostly, but he's very into solo sailing, lost control of his dinghy, and ripped up Mike's experimental raffia nets. He then managed to smudge the paint on Mike's newly painted transom. Mike was furious and told him he should stick to paddling in the lido. Jack refused to pay compensation and Mike accused him of thinking he was exempt from behaving like a responsible person and threatened to set the police on him!"

JACK SPRAT

"I'm not denying I was angry," exclaimed Jack. "But I did not kill him!" Any idea who did then? "I suspect it was Barnacle Bill. He sits all day on the end of the quay, talking dribble. He's claimed for years that he used to be an aide for some high-ranking naval officer and has sailed down the Amazon. Mike found out its all a tissue of lies—he used to be a dockhand on the Tyne. Mike was threatening to expose him as the liar he was!"

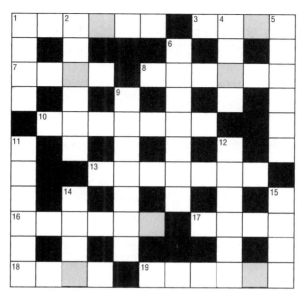

ACROSS

1 What Mike should put in his backbone (6)

3 Mike and Gary's weekly salary had dropped a bit lately (4)

7 Times are hard (4)

8 What Gary holds when thwarted (6)

10 It's just like this television detective (7)

13 Mike's wife once hit him over the head with this (7)

16 Jack is this sort of guy mostly (6)

17 Bill sits at the end of what all day (4)

18 Bill's greeting (4)

19 Gary likes to stick to the same old fishing grounds (6)

DOWN

1 Jack is into sailing alone (4)

2 Bill sailed down this river (6)

4 Bill claimed he used to be an assistant to a naval officer (4)

5 Mike accused Jack of thinking he was excused from behaving responsibly (6)

6 Bill talks nonsense (7)

9 Mike and Gary threw pails at each other (7)

11 The experimental nets were made of this (6)

12 Mike's wife would scold him (6)

14 Where Jack should stick to paddling (4)

15 Bill was a dockhand on which river (4)

Edited Out

The body of Eddie Tor has been found brutally strangled in the TV lounge at Sunset Towers Residential Home. As Superintendent U. Sless is being shown how the automatic floodgate works it is up to you to find out who the killer is.

MARVIN HAYE

"It was nigh time for somebody to delete the old boy!" exclaimed Marvin. "It was a slog getting on with him." Did he know who had killed him? "I think Win could be the one. She wanted to watch that musical about Eva Peron. Eddie said she should be more discriminating in what she watches, then told her she was a hideous old bag who looked like Medusa and ripped the lace curtain down and threw it over her head. The poor old girl was devastated!"

WIN BAGGE

"I didn't do it!" cried Win. "Although he used to be such a nice gent he had become very taxing recently." Any idea who had killed him. "It could have been Eric. He wanted to watch the Monaco Grand Prix on TV and Eddie told him that they should outlaw motor racing. He then went on to tell Eric that he was a broken reed now with no grit left, and he should go lose himself in the Irish Sea! Eric was very upset!"

ERIC IDLY

"It wasn't me!" declared Eric. "But I agree with Win that he used to be so nice—and he used to edit some lovely rustic magazines and had an exotic turn of phrase. Not now, though, his vocal ammo is aimed solely at hurting others!" Who did he think the killer was? "I'm afraid it was most likely Marvin. He was looking forward to watching a soccer documentary about Kevin Keegan—until Eddie said the man had about as much charisma as a can of creosote! That burst poor old Marvin's bubble!"

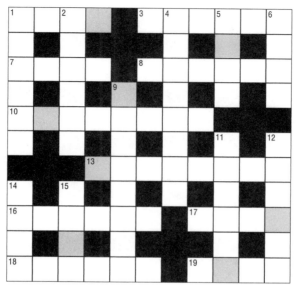

ACROSS

1 Eric is a broken one (4)
3 Which soccer player was the documentary about (6)
7 It was a grind getting on with Eddie (4)
8 He has become very draining recently (6)
10 The body of water (5, 3)
13 See **9D** (8)
16 Eddie thought Win resembled this gorgon (6)
17 The type of curtain thrown over her head (4)
18 They should do this to motor racing (6)
19 Eric should go and do this to himself in the **10A** (4)

DOWN

1 Some lovely what magazines (6)
2 This sort of turn of phrase (6)
4 The musical was about this person (3, 5)
5 Eric had no courage left now, according to Eddie (4)
6 It was about time (4)
9 The man had about as much of this as a can of **13A** (8)
11 Where the Grand Prix was being held (6)
12 Somebody should do this to the old boy, so says Marvin (6)
14 Eddie's vocal hail of bullets is solely to hurt others (4)
15 He used to do what to the magazines (4)

All Saintless Sinners

Another heinous crime has been committed—Doug Coller, pastor of All Saints, has been found brutally murdered behind the pulpit. Superintendent U. Sless has fallen into a newly dug grave, so it is once again up to you to find the culprit.

ABEL EAVE

"I'm the priest here, and in the pastor's absence, I will have to take Evensong, so let us get on with concluding this distasteful episode," pontificated Abel. Did he have any clues as to who could have killed Reverend Coller? "Well," he sniffed, "a minister of the cloth should be above childish enmities, but not so, I'm afraid. He and Helen Urth, who does the flowers, have a long-standing feud. Why, yesterday she used strong adhesive to stick corn dollies all around his treasured Renoir, and he hit the roof! She stormed out claiming that she would 'pay him back.' She's the one who did it."

HELEN URTH

"Absolute nonsense," she exclaimed, "the pastor and I are on very good terms. Abel would do a lot to discredit our friendship!" In her opinion, who is the culprit? "I rather suspect it is that disgusting deacon, Al, such an uncouth man. Why, only yesterday Doug found him sitting under the blackthorn, reading an Enid Blyton book as he devoured his foul oxtail soup, when he should have been clipping the yews! Doug only took him on because he is an orphan, and this is how he repays him. When challenged about his behavior, he just stood there looking foolish, rubbing that perpetual stye on his eye!"

AL MIGHTY

"She's a horrible old so-and-so," snarled Al, "under the illusion she's better than all of us, when she hasn't a fraction of the class the Reverend has." Had she done the dreadful deed then? "Na, she ain't got the guts," he opined. "If you was asking me, I'd say it was that la-di-da Abel—striding about with that big dog, Khan, at his heels, polishing the lens of his camera, taking pictures, making a note of this and that, trying to get rid of the pastor. He wants the living here, and he would kill to get it, you mark my words!"

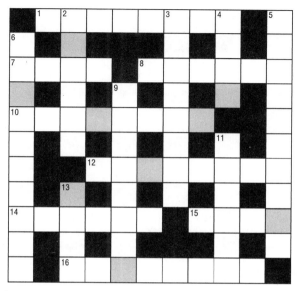

ACROSS

1 Helen has only a small piece of class (8)
7 What Abel was polishing (4)
8 Al's favorite novelist (6)
10 Puerile enmities (8)
12 Al ate his soup… (8)
14 And what flavor was it (6)
15 Big dog's name (4)
16 Abel had to take a church service (8)

DOWN

2 The pastor's treasured painting (6)
3 Helen was under the impression she was better than everyone (8)
4 Abel was making what of this and that (4)
5 Finishing the distasteful episode (10)
6 Tree for dining under (10)
9 Strong stuff for sticking (8)
11 No Ma or Pa, like Al (6)
13 Perpetual irritation (4)

Gardening with Attitude

Down at Flourishes Garden Center, the body of Rocky Bedd has been found brutally murdered. As Inspector U. Sless is stricken with hay fever it is up to you to catch the culprit.

TOM ATTOES

"What a to-do!" exclaimed Tom. "Poor Rocky, making an exit like that!" Did he know who had committed the murder? "I reckon it was Bertie—he and Rocky were opponents of old—there was always an issue over how to ventilate the greenhouses and should they extend the fruit cage! And the woven pots with a pleat in front that Bertie brought back from Yeovil were a big gaffe as far as Rocky was concerned—told Bertie to see an optician if he thought they would sell! Talk about fireworks!"

BERTIE LIZER

"Poppycock!" growled Bertie. "An overt attempt to get me into trouble!" Had he any ideas as to the killer? "That drip Walter ought to be your prime suspect—Rocky told him he was starting to look like a miniature zeppelin since he came off his vegan diet and Walter bopped him on the nose—just like Tyson! To add insult to injury, Rocky's dog Alfie then bit him on the backside!"

WALTER BARREL

"I didn't do it," whined Walter. "That's a horrible accusation to make!" Did he know who did then? "I wouldn't put it past Tom. He was always giving a little titbit here and there to the dog, which annoyed Rocky. And when he deadheaded the plants, he always managed to snip off the odd bud, too, which made Rocky recoil in anger, and when he went to the wholesalers, he always managed to obtain the wrong order. Rocky had had enough and told him so—so Tom murdered him!"

ACROSS

1 Bertie should see one of these (8)

7 The pots had this sort of fold down the front... (5)

8 ...which was a big mistake as far as Rocky was concerned (5)

9 Tom always managed to get the wrong order... (6)

10 ...when he visited the wholesalers (4)

12 Poor Rocky's way out (4)

14 Where the pots came from (6)

17 Bopped him, like this boxer (5)

18 Walter should be the prime suspect... (5)

19 ...and he looked like a miniature one (8)

DOWN

1 This sort of attempt to get Bertie into trouble (5)

2 Tom always gave a little morsel here and there to the dog (6)

3 Where the fruit was kept (4)

4 The dog's name (5)

5 Bertie and Rocky were enemies of old (9)

6 How to aerate greenhouses (9)

11 Deadheaded plants made Rocky jump back in anger (6)

13 There was always a problem over the greenhouses (5)

15 He came off this sort of diet (5)

16 What Tom managed to do to the odd bud (4)

Doggy Doings

The body of Vera Brash has been found brutally strangled behind the stage of the Much Muckle Village Hall after their annual dog show. As Superintendent U. Sless is scared of dogs it is up to you to find the culprit.

MAY FEINT

"What a total fiasco!" wailed May. "This is our own little Crufts kennel show and a great chance for all the canine lovers from miles around to hold a yearly reunion." Any idea as to the murderer? "Well, Eliza is a real possibility. When Vera's Great Dane escaped it headed straight for the rectory. That animal is built like a T-Rex and it smashed into the Rector's valuable icon hanging in the hall. He is away at present but Eliza knows her husband will be absolutely furious when he returns and blame her!"

ELIZA WRECK

"What an affront to my honor!" exclaimed Eliza. "I wonder how anyone imagines I could commit such a crime." Did she know who could? "Yes, indeed! When that animal left my house, it headed straight for Ina's. It got tangled in the drapes and brought it all down—swag, pole, the lot! It looked like a bomb had gone off in that house. It needed a stretch of effort to clean it all up. There's still a dab of the mess here and there. Ina was absolutely livid!"

INA SWOON

"Well, I certainly wouldn't confer the mantle of truth on her!" snorted Ina. "I think she is trying to abet that blasted dog in ruining my life!" Did she have a clue who the killer was? "It could be either of them but May is my bet. When the dog left my place it headed straight to the aviary built on the side of her house and ate this really cute parrot it managed to catch. What a sorry saga. It's a great shame the dog hasn't been put down as well!"

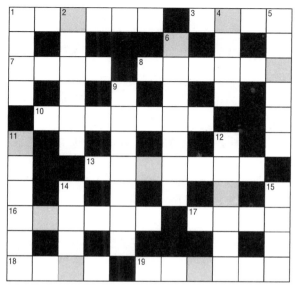

13

ACROSS

1 Ina wouldn't what with regards to the mantle of truth on Eliza (6)

3 What part of the house was the aviary built on (4)

7 What was the dog built like (1-3)

8 A great deal of work was **2D** to clean up Ina's house (6)

10 Where did Eliza live (7)

13 The dog show was a yearly what (7)

16 It was a total mess (6)

17 How much of the mess is left in Ina's house (1, 3)

18 What decorative part of the drapes came down, along with the pole (4)

19 The bird the dog ate (6)

DOWN

1 The bird was really this (4)

2 See **8A** (6)

4 What valuable item was smashed in Eliza's house (4)

5 Ina thinks it could be one or the other (6)

6 What Eliza said was an attack on her (7)

9 How much **8A** was needed to clean up the mess7)

11 The dog show was their own little what (6)

12 Eliza's surprise at being accused of a crime (6)

14 It was a sorry episode (4)

15 Ina thought Eliza was trying to help the dog to ruin her life (4)

Punitive Play-Acting

The body of Ima Prefect has been found in the changing rooms at Knowitall Academy.
As Superintendent U. Sless is in the playground playing hopscotch
it is up to you to solve the murder.

MAY DOITT

"What a to-do!" exclaimed May. "We were rehearsing for the annual eleventh-grade drama performance—we are doing *The Mikado*." Any clue to the killer? "It could be Dick—he always used to be male lead, thinks he's king of the heap, but this time Ima was in the star spot. He rebelled against it, of course, but any action he took was just a piece of juvenile idiocy—like the tunnel under the girls' dressing room!"

DICK BURPIN

"It certainly wasn't me!" stated Dick. "I'm not such a lame brain. Anyway I have a career lined up in NATO, so I'd be a mite stupid to ruin my chances." Did he know who did do it? "Sue was very jealous of Ima, who oozed chic. She was trying to undermine her health. I saw her scraping some asbestos off an old heatproof mat and scattering it around the alcove where Ima usually sits— but I reported it and the area was cleansed!"

SUE SPOTTY

"Pompous ass!" sniffed Sue. "No, I did not kill her!" In that case who did? "May was also jealous— she would defy stage directions to confuse Ima and then relent and behave herself. She was up and down like a yo-yo! But I saw her iron an awful crease into the costume Ima wears, and I also saw her trying to loosen the mounted ibex head so that it would fall on Ima's head!"

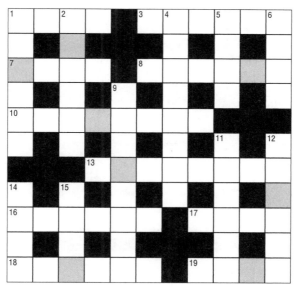

ACROSS

1 Dick would be a tad stupid (4)
3 Any deed was juvenile (6)
7 Dick thinks he is leader of the heap (4)
8 May would then give in and behave (6)
10 A **2D** under the girls' changing-room (8)
13 Dick revolted against it (8)
16 Sue was trying to undermine Ima's condition (6)
17 May was up and down like this toy (2-2)
18 This was ironed into Ima's costume (6)
19 May would disregard stage directions (4)

DOWN

1 The opera to be performed (6)
2 What was under the **10A** room (6)
4 After being reported the area was what (8)
5 The mounted head belonged to which animal (4)
6 Dick had a career lined up with this organization (initials) (4)
9 What the heatproof mat was made of (8)
11 The type of recess where Ima usually sits (6)
12 A piece of juvenile stupidity (6)
14 Ima oozed this (4)
15 Dick wasn't such a dim brain (4)

A Public Passing

Down at the Greasy Monkey Bar, bartender Mark Yeoman has been found dead with terrible slash wounds in the cellar. Superintendent U. Sless is busy investigating the quality of the beer in the parlor, so it is up to you to solve the crime on your own.

ED BUTTER

"This is a bit upsetting," Ed exclaimed. "Mark was the best player on our dart's team, and we were playing in a tournament tonight. I was going to try my new titanium darts. You don't need to be a magician to know we are one man short now!" Who could be behind this wanton crime? "My money's on that hairy arachnid, Hal Fwit—he's a right dumbbell," he snarled. "Mark was goalie on the bar's soccer team. Hal wanted that position and tried to bury him under the local construction site. He's mad enough to do anything!"

HAL FWIT

"I didn't do it," whined Hal. "I might not have had their advantages but I'm no murderer. Someone else did it!" And who might that be? "That Des Troyar, he's a mean one," snivelled Hal. "He was in Cuba for three months with his friend Williams, and the cops were going to intern him—he cracked a few skulls in Havana. And he hated Mark—clever guy, good-looking, very ornamental behind the bar! Charmed all the ladies. Des didn't like that one little bit!"

DES TROYAR

"Don't believe everything you hear," exclaimed Des. "Hal isn't all there and doesn't know the ins and outs of it!" So, tell us then, who killed the barman. "It was the landlord, Ed. Mark was trying to buy him out. You've got to hand it to the guy, he was a visual attraction, the customers loved him, and he would have made this place a roaring success. It's an airtight case—you've got the data. Ed's your man!"

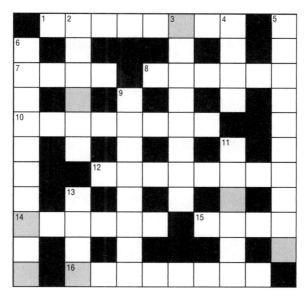

ACROSS

1 Des's friend (8)
7 You've got this information (4)
8 Who could be behind this unwarranted crime (6)
10 Completely sealed case (8)
12 You don't need to be an illusionist to know (8)
14 Mark's soccer position and Hal's ambition (6)
15 Havana's country (4)
16 Hal is this according to Ed (8)

DOWN

2 The police were going to imprison Des (6)
3 Hal was a hairy spider (8)
4 Mark was nearly under the local construction area (4)
5 Pretty as a picture behind the bar (10)
6 Hal might not have had these (10)
9 New darts made from this (8)
11 Mark was an optical attraction (6)
13 You've got to pass it to the guy (4)

Bed and Battered

Wendy Sunshine, proprietor of Sea View B&B, has been found murdered. As Superintendent U. Sless is testing the water temperature, it is up to you to apprehend the culprit.

SHELLEY BEECH

"How horrible!" cried Shelley. "Our guests will be shocked." Did she know who could have done it? "I think it was Sandy. She's definitely the odd man out here. She's a permanent guest, and lives in the attic, like an eagle in its eyrie, reading her Roald Dahl novels. She's a mean old thing, apt to resort to trickery to avoid paying rent. She's so angry now Wendy is going to sell up and retire to Malaga!"

SANDY COVE

"Nonsense!" snorted Sandy. "It won't occur to her that I can easily find another place to stay, will it?" Any ideas who might have done it then? "That smarmy Coral, I bet. When Wendy's friends Eric and Mary Roach came to dinner, she was all vermilion lips and nails, boasting of her trip to Iceland and the fantastic sleigh rides she went on. She's meant to be Wendy's chum, but treats her like dirt. She's also trying to buy Wendy's rural B&B, but Wendy isn't selling!"

CORAL BAY

"Really, what rubbish!" laughed Coral. "This theme happens to recur all the time about my trying to buy that place. I don't want it!" Did she have any clues who had done it then? "I think it was poor Shelley, worked like a Trojan about the place, but a triple fool—Wendy used her abominably! She cooked a beautiful pilau last night and Wendy told her it was swimming in lard! And she made a delicious rosemary-flavored jelly, and Wendy threw it out and said it was insipid. Poor Shelley was in tears!"

16

ACROSS

1 The flavor of the dessert (8)

7 Sandy was like an eagle in its what (5)

8 The first name of a favored author (5)

9 Where Wendy was going to retire (6)

10 Coral was meant to be Wendy's friend (4)

12 The beautiful dish was swimming in this (4)

14 Shelley worked like one (6)

17 It wouldn't dawn on Shelley that Sandy could easily find another place to stay (5)

18 What was the beautiful meal (5)

19 Sandy would resort to deceit (8)

DOWN

1 The location of Wendy's other B&B (5)

2 The type of rides had in Iceland (6)

3 & **4D** Wendy's female friend (4)

4 See **3D** (5)

5 The color of the lips and nails (9)

6 Sandy was the black sheep (3, 3, 3)

11 Shelley was this many times a fool (6)

13 This theme seems to come up again all the time (5)

15 What type of dessert was made, and thrown out (5)

16 **3D**'s husband (4)

Wick-ed!

The body of Bob Aboute has been found murdered in the garage attached to the side of his house in Little Wick. Superintendent U. Sless has once again lost his way so it is up to you to catch the murderer.

LIZA ALLOT

"How dreadful!" stated Liza as she munched on a pretzel. "That someone killed him." Any idea who did? "I know he and Mona have had problems—she found a manila envelope in his desk and inside were some airline tickets from El Al, all for one person. He was going to take off to Latvia, Siberia, Israel, and heaven's know where—I've even heard him brushing up on his Hebrew. Indeed, when I confronted him, he gave me an evil leer and offered to take me, too! Mona obviously wasn't able to cope with that!"

MONA ABOUTE

"Nonsense!" exclaimed Mona. "Bob has long desired to travel. He was the finest husband around. We were amazed anew each day at our strong love for each other." Any clue as to the killer, then? "Try old Tom—they've had a long standing feud for years! He sits outside his semi-detached house everyday, hardly moving, staring like a lizard, moving only to complain. His latest moan is about the load of manure we had deposited on the drive yesterday. Says it smells and is drawing flies. They had a terrible quarrel about it!"

TOM TATTLE

"Load of rubbish!" laughed Tom. "Those two have always made a comical pair!" Did he know who had done it then? "Yeah, I reckon it was Liza. Sick of being a widow—wouldn't mind her best friend's husband. She staged an elaborate skid in her Mini the other day, in front of him! Climbed out wheezing with that asthma of hers and he held her and stroked her head until she calmed. She fed him a samosa or several—which he has always had a passion for! She was trying desperately to get her hooks into him but he turned her down—hell hath no fury. She's your culprit!"

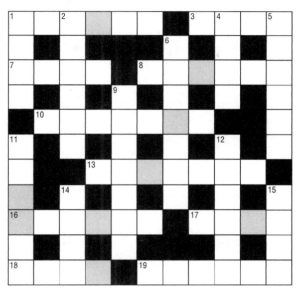

ACROSS

1 Bob had a passion for this food (6)

3 The airline he was booked on (2, 2)

7 The car Liza drives (4)

8 He was the greatest husband, according to Mona (6)

10 What Liza was munching on (7)

13 What a laughable pair do Bob and Mona make (7)

16 The language Bob was brushing up on (6)

17 Bob's house is in Little— (4)

18 Bob and Mona were amazed afresh each day (4)

19 Tom stared like this creature (6)

DOWN

1 What sort of detached house Tom had (4)

2 What was deposited on the drive (6)

4 Bob gave Liza an evil what (4)

5 The Baltic country Bob had tickets for (6)

6 And the cold region he was also going to (7)

9 Bob caressed Liza's head (7)

11 Her medical condition (6)

12 The envelope the tickets were in (6)

14 Mona obviously wasn't adept to cope with that (4)

15 Liza staged an elaborate slide (4)

Washed Out!

Down at the Shingle Bay Fish Cannery the horribly strangled body of Angie O'Gram has been found in the ladies bathroom. As Superintendent U. Sless has been nipped by a crab, you must once again solve the crime.

ISA BELL

"She was a lazy piece of work!" claimed Isa. "She was one to gallop off to the ladies bathroom at every available opportunity to peruse the latest Judith Krantz novel!" Any idea who killed her? "Our forewoman, recently appointed to the role, used to get very cross with her. Angie was apt to skip fish as it came past on the roller and then Barbie would find granules of sand amongst it. That sort of thing tends to ruin the quality of the finished product!"

BARBIE DROLL

"Yes, indeed it does!" agreed Barbie. "However, I did not kill her!" Did she know who did? "She used to be good friends with Rachel, but something terrible happened. Angie looked after her gerbil while she was away but unfortunately it died. Then it got mixed up with some ground veal that was used to fill a tortilla shell at a church picnic held during our recent Indian summer! Poor Rachel, did she ever yelp when she heard about it!"

RACHEL BUNTER

"I certainly did!" said Rachel. "But I'm not the murderer!" Who is then? "I think it was Isa. She used to use Angie's house as a refuge as the harmony in her marriage began to fade. Then Angie began to change—first, each ear lobe was pierced for several earrings. Next, a very fetching pair of suede culottes. Then it was all explained. Isa found her lying in an attitude of complete abandon on a fleece under the trees in the back garden, feeding a succulent looking omelette to Isa's husband, and both of them clearly enjoying themselves enormously!"

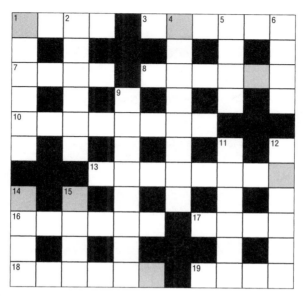

ACROSS

1 That sort of thing tends to impair the quality (4)

3 The fish came past on what (6)

7 The harmony in Isa's marriage began to grow dim (4)

8 The animal Angie was looking after (6)

10 Barbie would find these small particles of sand (8)

13 The meat was put in this at the picnic (8)

16 Novelist Judith's surname (6)

17 The dead animal was mixed with ground what (4)

18 To read, as Angie did (6)

19 Rachel let out a what when she heard about her pet (4)

DOWN

1 Isa used Angie's house as a sanctuary (6)

2 The type of summer weather they had for the picnic (6)

4 What Angie was feeding Isa's husband (8)

5 The part of the ear Angie had pierced—several times (4)

6 Barbie's recently appointed what (4)

9 Angie was wearing a **15D** of what (8)

11 And what she was lying on (6)

12 Her pace in going to the ladies' bathroom (6)

14 Angie was apt to leave out fish as it came past on the roller (4)

15 See **9D** (4)

W.I. Stitched Up!

The President of the Peachy Bottom Women's Institute, Iris Bloom, has been found poisoned by hand unknown at the weekly sale of work. Superintendent U. Sless is trying his hand at crocheting, so it is up to you to solve the murder and discover where the poison was concealed.

PEARL STITCH

"What a dreadful thing," exclaimed Pearl, "but it is not really a surprise—Iris was very arrogant and overbearing, and very boastful! When her daughter married into the Mowlam family, her chest diameter swelled by twelve inches. Honeymoon in Rhodesia, before it became Zimbabwe, don't you know? Sickening!" Any ideas on the murderer? "Ah, well, you don't have to be a genius to know it could have been absolutely anybody, but my guess is Cara Twine. Iris was so insulting about her mandarin orange wine—too sweet and far too much sediment! Poor Cara couldn't stop crying. I think she did it."

CARA TWINE

"Oh, no, that's awful," twittered Cara. "I couldn't do something so horrible. Iris was a little forceful at times but I had great respect for her. My daughter was a bridesmaid at the wedding. We're all very close." In that case, who could have killed Iris—any clues? "Well," simpered Cara, "I would think Coco is a prime suspect. Her husband Amos has always been a staunch defender of Iris in any disagreement. And when Iris told Coco her Chocolate Bombe Surprise looked like a particularly malformed grain silo—Amos laughed! Coco was livid."

COCO NUTTE

"Rubbish," snorted Coco, "I didn't do it. Look hard enough and anyone has the ammunition to accuse all and sundry of killing her." Could she tell us the identity of the murderer? "Pearl, without a doubt," asserted Coco. "A very proud woman, of similar ilk to Iris. Pearl caused quite an affray when Iris called the nile-green cardigan, with the ruff around the neck, totally revolting. Pearl threatened to call up an armada of relations to trample her prized garden to shreds! She's got a temper!"

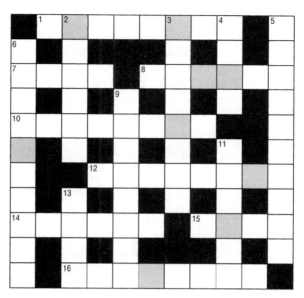

ACROSS

1 Cara's wine (8)
7 It was around the neck (4)
8 Politically correct family to marry into (6)
10 This, around Iris' chest, swelled rather a lot (8)
12 You don't want to find this in the bottom of your glass (8)
14 A fleet of relations (6)
15 A malformed grain container (4)
16 It won't spring one on you, knowing she's dead (8)

DOWN

2 Pearl caused a commotion (6)
3 Where the honeymooners went (8)
4 The green of the revolting cardigan (4)
5 Anyone had enough of this to make accusations (10)
6 Always the..., never the bride (10)
9 **13D** was a staunch... (8)
11 You needn't be a mastermind to know anybody could have done it (6)
13 Coco's husband (4)

Friends Indeed!

The brutally battered body of Eliza Badun has been found in a bedroom of a house shared by four friends. Superintendent U. Sless has had his car towed and is retrieving it from the pound, so it is again up to you to apprehend the culprit.

PENNY PINCHER

"What a dreadful thing to happen!" exclaimed Penny. "Who did it, I wonder?" No ideas then? "Well, Tina could have—they had a falling out during their vacation in Aspen. Tina got tipsy one night and tripped over a coyote and broke her ankle. Eliza didn't miss her till morning, then had to call the infantry out to find her! Tina said it was a deliberate attempt to get rid of her and tried to whack her with her crutch. Eliza is quite burly and fought her off, but Tina fell over and got a thorn in her breast, which festered. They've hardly spoken a word since!"

TINA BOPPER

"Utter nonsense," snorted Tina. "She's nuts! I didn't do it!" In that case, who did? "Carina, without a doubt! She has been stuffing herself with chocolate for weeks, and Eliza told her she resembled a suet pudding, sitting cross-legged on a pile of cushions looking like a blissful inmate of some eastern harem. I've never seen Carina so hurt and upset—she actually threatened Eliza!"

CARINA RIVER

"Rubbish," cried Carina. "I'm not violent!" Any clues then as to the culprit? "Probably Penny. It was a constant battle between the two of them for the upper hand. As usual, Eliza was able to equip herself with the most hurtful observations. Penny has been using cosmetics made from aloe leaf and Eliza said it would be of more help to adorn herself with cow muck! Penny was furious and very nearly moved out to live with her sister Anna, but we persuaded her to stay. That was a mistake!"

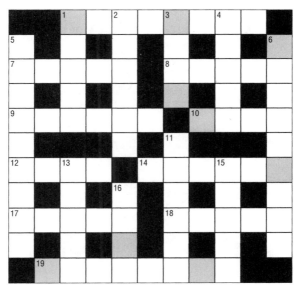

ACROSS

1 Carina looked in this happy type of mood (8)
7 Some eastern what (5)
8 Eliza was able to tool herself up (5)
9 The animal Tina tripped over (6)
10 The plant used for cosmetics (4)
12 The part of the plant used (4)
14 What Tina tried to whack Eliza with (6)
17 This caused festering (5)
18 Where the vacation was (5)
19 This had to be called out to find Tina (8)

DOWN

1 Eliza is quite well built (5)
2 A resident of an eastern collective (6)
3 A type of pudding that Carina resembled (4)
4 As normal, as Eliza was able to (5)
5 Carina stuffed herself with sweet stuff (9)
6 It was a constant battle to gain this (5, 4)
11 What part of the body festered (6)
13 It would be more help to decorate with cow muck (5)
15 Tina got drunk on vacation (5)
16 Penny's sister (4)

Fowl Play

The brutally battered body of Wes Stirring has been found murdered in the garden of his home. As Superintendent U. Sless has been trapped by a swarm of bees it is up to you to solve the crime.

ALFIE FINE

"Absolutely incredible!" exclaimed Alfie. "Now I have lost my regular canasta partner!" Any idea who had killed him? "His wife, I believe. She's been haranguing him for a long time about the dry rot in the house. She even called him from Dyce Airport when she arrived in Aberdeen to visit her family. Poor man, he went down to the local bar, The Yeomen, and downed a liberal amount of Scotch! They liked him in there.

He was a big tipper."

VERA STIRRING

"Poor man indeed!" snorted Vera. "He just liked to play the errant husband, occasionally." Any notion who the killer was then? "Our son, Ben. He has been looking forward to his chance to turn a tidy profit on the sale of our garnet collection for years. I shudder when I consider that he is actually related to me! Wes had even lent him money so that he could pay his fare so that he could go and live in Scotland, but apparently that wasn't good enough for him—he wanted everything!"

BEN STIRRING

"How dreary my dear mother is!" drawled Ben. "No, it was not me that killed my father." Who did then? "My guess is Alfie. I was playing I-spy with my kid the other day when I heard a flurry in the chicken coop. There he was, surreptitiously wringing the necks of some of Father's prize hens! Oh-oh, I thought, and called in the cavalry—in the person of my father. There was was a fight and Father wasn't even able to attain a tiny amount of compensation. I do believe there was mention of the police being called in—so Alfie did him in!"

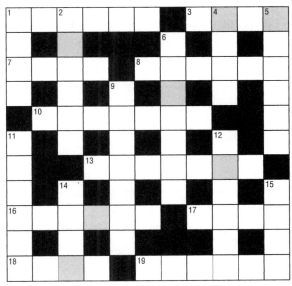

ACROSS

1 Vera harangued Wes about this (3, 3)
3 Vera was Wes's spouse (4)
7 The chickens' home (4)
8 Wes was a big one (6)
10 Vera shudders that she is part of Ben's family (7)
13 Wes was Alfie's regular partner for a card game (7)
16 Ben heard a hubbub in the henhouse (6)
17 The money for Ben's ticket to Scotland (4)
18 The meager compensation Wes couldn't even get (4)
19 The jewel collection Ben wanted sold (6)

DOWN

1 The airport Vera called from (4)
2 The name of the local bar (6)
4 The game Ben was playing (1-3)
5 The type of husband Wes liked to play (6)
6 This amount of Scotch (7)
9 Ben called in the what (7)
11 See **14D** (6)
12 Wes wasn't able to get compensation (6)
14 Ben was looking forward to his chance to make a tidy **11D** from the collection (4)
15 Wes loaned Ben the money (4)

Vandal Vanquished

The brutally murdered body of Barry Dyed has been found at the back of the Fat Landlady Coffee House in Cold Harbor. As Superintendent U. Sless is busy dodging the seagulls it is up to you to catch the culprit.

CLAIRE WINNER

"Och, that lad was a terrible layabout!" exclaimed Claire. Did she know who had killed him? "I think it was his friend, Steve. He couldn't wake him in the mornings. Barry spent half his life in bed—I'm surprised he didn't take root. The other half of his life was spent drinking and vandalizing, with that loud ghetto blaster hoisted to his shoulder. He had no job, therefore no money. Steve has a job as a teller in the Wilson Bank, just down the street, and was fed up with subbing for him!"

STEVE NEVEN

"Nosy, isn't she!" laughed Steve. "Wish she'd take a hike back to Loch Ness, or whatever Scottish isle she came from." Any clue as to who did it? "His girlfriend Jude has had enough of him. He was becoming boring. She's into nest-building but he wasn't a suitable candidate. All he seemed to do apart from sleep was swig cans of beer or down bottles of his mother's sloe gin! But get in his way and he'd give you a once-over you wouldn't forget. No, Jude didn't want a rough thug like him and got rid of him—permanently!"

JUDE BORE

"It wasn't me!" stormed Jude. "You'll have to look elsewhere!" Like where? "The fat landlady herself! Barry poured lychee pudding all over her fake ocelot coat. She was livid! Then she caught him trying to pry a fancy tile off the wall, over by the side gate. An elevator couldn't have hit the roof as quick as she did! She tried to locate the local cop to have him arrested but couldn't find him, so I reckon she took matters into her own hands!"

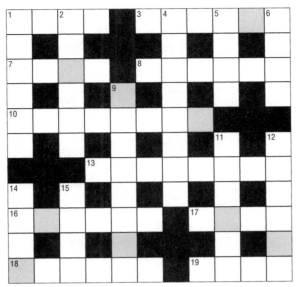

22

ACROSS

1 Barry was trying to pry a fancy one off the wall (4)

3 He was becoming this for Jude (6)

7 Ness is one of these (4)

8 Claire's coat was fake animal fur (6)

10 She could hit the roof faster than this (8)

13 Barry might do this, the amount of time he spent in bed (4, 4)

16 The name of the bank where Steve worked (6)

17 Steve couldn't do this to Barry in the mornings (4)

18 Barry had a what blaster on his shoulder (6)

19 Jude was into building this (4)

DOWN

1 Steve's position at the bank (6)

2 The fruit pudding poured over the coat (6)

4 Barry would give you this if you got in his way (4-4)

5 Scottish place Claire came from (4)

6 The wall was by the side entrance (4)

9 Barry was a terrible slob (8)

11 Claire tried to find the local cop (6)

12 The bank was just down the road (6)

14 He was always taking what from beer cans (4)

15 Or drinking this gin (4)

Teenage Terror

Superintendent U. Sless has been asked to investigate the killing of a young man, Brian Storm, at a birthday party at the Blattley Village Hall. He has unfortunately got his car stuck in a ditch so it is up to you to solve the murder.

MAY CAKILLIN

"He was my boyfriend and I can't imagine anyone wanting to kill him," wailed May. "He was eighteen today, this was his party!" Did she have any ideas who might be responsible? "I think it was that Cleo—she's always causing trouble for him! He used to go out with her. He hired a rental car and took her and her brother Oswald to a Spice Girls concert once, and she stripped and leaped on the stage! He wasn't exactly ecstatic about that and broke up with her. She's been trying to get back at him ever since!"

CLEO ROUT

"What a lot of drivel," stormed Cleo. "That would be a nice, neat, clinical answer for her—see her rival off well and good, that would!" If it wasn't her, who was it then? "His so-called best friend, Joe. He was very jealous of Brian. He was a big strapping kid, would always prod people out of his way. All us girls thought he was wonderful. That little gnat Joe, would like him out of the way!"

JOE CALLOT

"You don't kill your friend over something like that!" laughed Joe. "That would be a bit stupid, wouldn't it?" Has he any clue who did it, then? "That May, I think she's the one. It's mildly ironic, really: sweet little vicarage miss, avid reader of Danielle Steele—butter wouldn't melt in her mouth! Last week, I found her drunk on elderberry wine, a dead plover at her feet—she'd stabbed it with her tweezers! Brian was going to give her the old heave-ho, and I don't think she'd take that too well!"

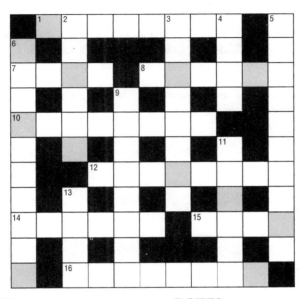

ACROSS

1 Brian's age (8)

7 How Brian moved people out of his way (4)

8 The brother's name (6)

10 See **4D** (8)

12 First name of a famous novelist (8)

14 The car was hired (6)

15 Cleo has tried to get back at him since when (4)

16 Poor little **11D** was stabbed with these (8)

DOWN

2 May's behavior is mildly humorous (6)

3 Brian wasn't happy after the concert (8)

4 & **10A** The answer would be nice and what else (4)

5 Flavor of the wine (10)

6 The group at the concert (5, 5)

9 A sweet little miss from the rectory (8)

11 See **16A** (6)

13 Joe's a little insect (4)

Do-It-Yourself Destruction

The body of Polly Sell has been found brutally murdered in the storeroom of the Much Muckle Home Decoration Store. Superintendent U. Sless is busy comparing wallpaper samples so it is up to you to find the culprit.

MATT FINNISH

"What an agreeable surprise!" laughed Matt. "Somebody has at long last finished the old virago off!" Any ideas who that somebody might be? "Probably Anna. They've been rivals for years. When Anna came back from vacationing in Aden, talking about her new boyfriend, Bobby, with the Midas touch, Polly promptly went off on a bird-watching break in Guernsey, and returned waxing lyrical about this erne and that eider. They're both as miserable as Eeyore."

ANNA GLYPTER

"Utter nonsense!" snorted Anna. "So, that's his gambit, is it? Essential to ensure suspicion is cast on somebody else!" And who should suspicion be cast on? "Try Woody for size. He seems to lurch from one catastrophe to another. Left all the farm gates open on his way to work and the local cop had to give him a warning. Polly was like a spitting cobra—the cows ate all the flowers in her window boxes!"

WOODY CHIP

"I didn't do it!" cried Woody. "You're making a grave error in assuming I did." So who did then? "I think it was Matt. Polly was a gutsy lady who built this business up from scratch, but he seems to undermine her at every turn. You name it, he'll ruin it. He bought a load of bathroom fixtures, in yellow plastic, on a whim and she hit the roof because we can't sell them! And he only ordered a single faucet. They have to be orderd in pairs so she got mad and told him to clear out."

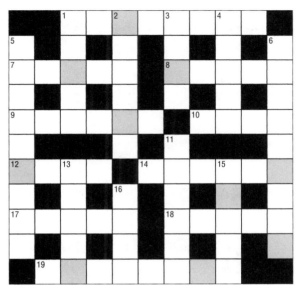

ACROSS

1 Where the bird-watching break took place (8)

7 What Woody left open (5)

8 What sort of touch did the new boyfriend have (5)

9 The two women were as miserable as this donkey (6)

10 & **4D** The birds Polly was waxing lyrical about (4)

12 Where Anna had her vacation (4)

14 Matt's opening maneuver (6)

17 Woody did this from one catastrophe to another (5)

18 Polly was like this snake (5)

19 Polly immediately went on break (8)

DOWN

1 Woody thought Polly was a brave lady (5)

2 Make certain, as Matt was trying to do (6)

3 Give it this and Matt will ruin it (4)

4 See **10A** (5)

5 This sort of surprise (9)

6 Vital it is, casting suspicion on others (9)

11 Matt only ordered one of these (6)

13 A grave mistake, assuming Woody did it (5)

15 Anna's boyfriend (5)

16 Matt bought the fixtures on this type of impulse (4)

Animal Crackers

The badly beaten body of Lee Valone has been found in the office of the Little Wick Animal Sanctuary. Superintendent U. Sless has fallen in the duck pond so it is up to you to find the culprit.

BEAU NIDLE

"I must say, Lee was a bit of a despot!" exclaimed Beau. "But I wouldn't have expected this!" Any idea who had done it? "Pat was always in tears after encounters with Lee— they were always having fights. He hit the roof yesterday when he found that Beatrix, our adorable wombat, who has a fetish for booze, had been into his VSOP brandy. Pat seems to pursue a career of one mishap after another. Lee had warned her that her employment here was under constant review!"

PAT PETTS

"Well, I never!" cried Pat, tossing back her mane of lustrous blonde hair. "It wasn't me, I couldn't harm a fly." Did she know who had then? "I think it was Ben—he was always in trouble. He was exercising Lucifer yesterday—a beautiful stallion rescued from some mine in Asia—when the poor horse put his foreleg down a defunct well, and fell. He broke his leg and had to be put down. Ben ended up with a couple of crushed ribs. Lee was so enraged, his speech came out a garbled croak. Ben's job was on the line!"

BEN SLACK

"What rubbish!" snorted Ben. "I didn't do it." Who did then? "It was Beau—he's no saint! His mantle of responsibility has been slipping lately. He allowed Edward and Alberta, our pair of Canadian geese, to escape into the veggie garden. They decimated the runner bean seedlings and suffered terribly for their greed. Lee's explosion was like Etna and Vesuvius rolled into one—we all thought he was going to strike Beau. Lee told Beau he'd be hitting the road any day now!"

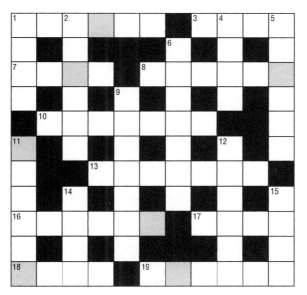

ACROSS

1 The adorable animal with a **12D** for alcohol (6)

3 Pat tossed back her lustrous blonde hair (4)

7 Ben's job was on the what (4)

8 Pat's employment was under constant analysis (6)

10 & **5D** The names of the geese (7)

13 The stallion's name (7)

16 Lee's what came out a garbled croak (6)

17 Ben ended up with a couple of these crushed (4)

18 One of the volcanoes Lee resembled (4)

19 See **11D** (6)

DOWN

1 What the horse put his leg down (4)

2 Beau's veneer of responsibility was slipping (6)

4 The continent the stallion was rescued from (4)

5 See **10A** (6)

6 The name of **1A** (7)

9 **1D** was not working anymore (7)

11 Pat seems to follow a career of one **19A** after another (6)

12 See **1A** (6)

14 The runner seedlings were decimated (4)

15 The sort of brandy Lee liked (initials) (4)

Checked-out Charlie

The body of Charlie Farlie has been found brutally murdered in his study.
As Superintendent U. Sless is admiring the mosaics in the hallway it is up to you
to catch the culprit.

ARTY FICIAL

"Harmless old guy!" mourned Arty. "Why should anyone want to kill him?" Did he have any idea?
"His nephew Larry would be my guess. He was trying to hoodwink him out of money so he
could buy a cottage he'd found in Clovelly. Charlie knew what a spendthrift he was, but the boy
was resolute in his attempts to gain access to the private papers in Charlie's desk."

LARRY KIN

"It wasn't me!" exclaimed Larry. "But he was a penny-pinching old miser!" Who was it then?
"I wouldn't put it past my cousin Vi. She used to waylay him when he was on a ramble in the
country. Benn Woods was a favorite place of his, but he was very wary when he approached the
valley in case she discovered it. She felt he shouldn't deduct anything from her allowance and
her board and lodging should be free. Trouble is, she blew all her money on the cinema, or else
that skinny boyfriend of hers!"

VI LENT

"I didn't do it!" cried Vi. "I was fond of my uncle!" In that case did she know who had done it?
"His friend Arty could have done it. When Uncle Charlie retired, he was so elated at the accolade
he received from the chairperson—Lady Emma. It also came with substantial financial rewards!
Arty kicked up a rumpus, because he felt that as the senior partner in the company, all kudos
should have been his!"

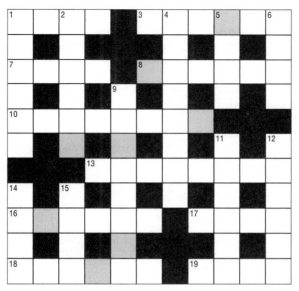

ACROSS

1 Where the private papers were (4)
3 Vi would waylay Charlie when he was on a walk (6)
7 Vi thinks Arty might have — it (4)
8 Larry would try to gain a way to Charlie's private papers (6)
10 The cottage Larry wanted was in this village (8)
13 Larry was trying to trick him out of his money (8)
16 Arty kicked up this (6)
17 The name of the woods (4)
18 Charlie was so happy, when he retired, at his **4D** (6)
19 Charlie was very cautious when he approached the **7A** (4)

DOWN

1 Vi felt her uncle shouldn't take away anything from her allowance (6)
2 Arty was a partner in the company (6)
4 See **18A** (8)
5 Vi threw away all her money (4)
6 Or, otherwise on her **12D** boyfriend (4)
9 Larry was determined in his attempts (8)
11 Vi spent all her money at the movies (6)
12 See **6D** (6)
14 Vi thought board and lodging should be this (4)
15 The name of the chairwoman (4)

Ice Breaker

The body of Kiki De Butt has been found at Cold Harbor Ice Rink, on the day of the grand opening. Unfortunately, Superintendent U. Sless has slipped on the ice and broken his ankle, so you are required to continue the investigation.

MOLLY ERRED

"What a disgraceful occurrence when, in my capacity as Lady Mayoress, I am about to open our ice-skating rink," declared Molly. "I really would expect people to be a little more discreet! My husband, the minister, will be most displeased!" Has she any clues as to who could have been so indiscreet as to commit murder, then? "Yes, indeed. That awful Mickey, who was going out with my au pair! He wanted to marry her, but she intended to return to Sweden. He was livid, and threatened to beat her up!"

MICKEY TAKER

"What flimsy evidence to accuse a man of murder!" snarled Mickey. "What a snob! She needs to look closer to home!" So how close? "Her husband, that close. Leslie was hanging around Kiki all the time, displaying dash and elan, thinking he was a man of allure. He tried to get around her but she pushed him in the river near the picnic site and smashed the ignition in his Rover! He's terrified his wife will find out!"

REVEREND ERRED

"Nonsense! How absurd to accuse me of such behavior and such a crime!" exclaimed the reverend. "Never could I carry on in that godless manner!" In that case, did he have any ideas as to who carried out the killing? "I am afraid so—however irrelevant and untrue Mickey's statement is, my wife believed I was behaving in an improper fashion with Kiki. She is a little unbalanced at present, and as a rule sits around drinking Earl Grey tea and eating Spam® sandwiches, holding imaginary conversations with the gentry. When she heard Kiki was to return to Sweden, she became very irrational at the loss of her services and killed her!"

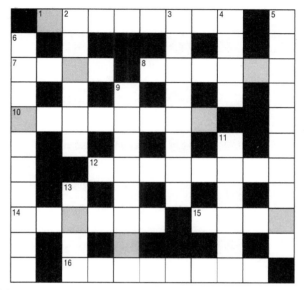

27

ACROSS

1 In her capacity as what was Molly going to open the rink (8)
7 As a habit, Molly sits around (4)
8 She is a bit unbalanced (6)
10 Molly's favorite tea (4, 4)
12 What she expects people to be (8)
14 Her type of nanny (2, 4)
15 The reverend's dash and flair, maybe (4)
16 Molly's husband, the clergyman (8)

DOWN

2 He thought he was a man of appeal (6)
3 The proof was rather flimsy, to accuse a man of murder (8)
4 Kiki pushed Leslie in the river near the picnic area (4)
5 What sort of rink was to be opened (3-7)
6 However immaterial and untrue Mickey's statement might have been (10)
9 What was smashed in the Rover (8)
11 The first name of the husband (6)
13 Teatime sandwiches (4)

Masterful Murder

The body of Jim Master has been found behind his bar in the village of Pleasant Pastures. Superintendent U. Sless has been asked to change a keg so it is up to you to apprehend the culprit.

DR. EVAN ELPAS

"I'm not surprised!" exclaimed Evan. "A rough diamond, that Jim." Any ideas who could have killed him? "Diplomat Pat! He was a consul in Tokyo, then retired here, to his Utopia as he called it, became a freemason, then along comes Jim and ruins the tone of this place. Pat was vocal in his condemnation of him so Jim wouldn't let him enter the bar again—Pat saw this as an attempt to lower his status in the village. I have an idea this pushed him over the edge!"

PAT TREFIED

"Rubbish!" snorted Pat. "I didn't kill him." Any clue as to who did? "The vicar. Morgan has been thoroughly corrupted by Jim—the two of them would go down to the gym to 'pump iron' together, then trek over to the bar to play poker and drink! Then they would prowl around the village, evocative of Vikings out to maraud, pestering the young women. Morgan's living is in grave danger!"

MORGAN PIPE

"I certainly didn't do it!" said Morgan. "Things are not as black as Pat has painted!" Any thoughts on who did do it? "Indeed, yes. The doctor. He does excel in his medical practice and were he still in a London hospital, would reach the acme of his profession. Unfortunately, he had a disagreement with Jim and in the ensuing fracas, Jim's ulna was broken, his optic nerve damaged, along with a pecan pie in the bar. The cleanser used to clean the broken arm caused a severe reaction and Jim was threatening to sue!"

ACROSS

1 What the two men did at the gym (4, 4)
7 Morgan's profession (5)
8 Jim wouldn't let Pat go in the pub again (5)
9 What Pat used to be in Japan (6)
10 Evan could have reached this in his profession (4)
12 The two men would walk over to the bar (4)
14 Pat retired to his dream place (6)
17 Pat was loquacious in his condemnation of Jim (5)
18 The city where Pat used to work (5)
19 What was put on the broken arm and caused a reaction (8)

DOWN

1 The type of pie that was broken (5)
2 The two men were out to plunder (6)
3 Evan had one about Pat (4)
4 The damaged nerve (5)
5 It was reminiscent of Vikings (9)
6 Pat became one when he retired (9)
11 Pat thought it was an attempt to lower his what (6)
13 Evan does very well in his medical practice (5)
15 The card game played at the bar (5)
16 The bone that was broken (4)

Bated Breath

The body of Rowdy Bates has been found badly beaten about the head, in the village of Little Wick. As Superintendent U. Sless is held up in a highway traffic jam, it is up to you to catch the killer.

SAM SENSE

"No surprise that punk has been killed!" stated Sam. "He's been a cancer on the face of this community ever since the family emigrated from Ontario a couple of years ago." Any idea who killed him? "Old Farmer Huw was always after him. As a gag Rowdy painted Nutmeg, Huw's prize calf, a glorious ruby color just before the county show! What an ensuing palaver—Huw was heard to avow he would get even!"

HUW WOODS

"To be sure, that kid deserved all he got!" exclaimed Huw. "But it wasn't me." In that case did he know who it was? "Fred seems a likely bet. He was forever chasing Rowdy off his land. Fred has caused a small tributary of the Adur to deviate through his property and had started a very successful carp farming business. He found Rowdy and a throng of his friends trying to poach the fish at night. We have it on record that he was 'going to get Rowdy'!"

FRED PIKE

"It certainly wasn't me!" stormed Fred, "although I would have liked to wring the boy's neck!" Any clue to the identity of the killer? "Sam is quick to lay blame on others, but I think it was him. He's been a tailor in this village for many years, and a good one—you would have to comb the south to find better. Rowdy was racing around on his quad bike—Sam began to fidget as the boy got closer to the shop and all of a sudden—crash! Right through the decorative lattice door and into the actual shop! Sam had to close for several weeks for the repairs. Lost a lot of business, and money!"

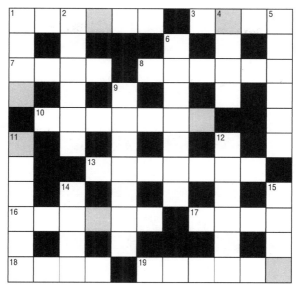

ACROSS

1 The name of Huw's prized animal (6)

3 And what it was (4)

7 The fish Fred farmed (4)

8 Huw said they had it on archive that Fred was going to get Rowdy (6)

10 Where Rowdy's family had emigrated from (7)

13 A decorative fretwork door (7)

16 As the lad got nearer to the shop (6)

17 On what sort of bike (4)

18 The glorious color **1A** was painted (4)

19 Sam's occupation (6)

DOWN

1 Fred would like to wring this part of Rowdy's anatomy (4)

2 Fred found Rowdy and this crowd of friends (6)

4 Huw was heard to pledge that he would get even (4)

5 Sam began to twitch (6)

6 Fred caused the river to turn through his land (7)

9 The ensuing fuss (7)

11 Rowdy had been this on the face of the community (6)

12 And drove his bike right into the veritable shop (6)

14 You would have to search the south to find a better **19A** (4)

15 The name of the river (4)

30

Seductive Sensation

Private Eye Noel Uck has been found brutally murdered in his seedy office.
As Superintendent U. Sless is busy inspecting the hall with a very large magnifying glass,
it is up to you to conduct the investigation.

APRIL SHOWERS

"Serves him right!" sniffed April. "He thought he was glamorous, like something out of *Dallas*,
but he was really just a clumsy oaf." Any idea who killed him? "Alice was originally quite taken in
by his veneer of sophistication and the air of mystery created by his fedora hat! He used both to
lure gullible young girls like her back to his lair. A glass or two of cola, a fatherly game of ludo,
and she was hooked. Then cast off like a worn coat. These things leave a scar for life!"

ALICE BAND

"I didn't do it!" cried Alice. "I thought he loved me!" Did she know who had done it? "Hope was
taken in by him as well. She hired him to find her boyfriend, whom she was keen to locate,
seeing as half her assets had also gone with him. After detailed analysis, he spun a yarn about
some deed that needed clarification and invited her into his office. After downing an aperitif or
several, obviously designed to impair her judgment, she was in his arms! And then there was
another cast off!"

HOPE SPRINGS

"Lies and nonsense!" snorted Hope. "I didn't kill him, although I admit to being taken in by him!"
Who did kill him then? "April, for my money. He certainly tried an entirely different approach
with her. Behaving like a hand-washing lackey, showing a robust desire to help her trace her
errant husband. After a brief synopsis of events, he was unable to curb himself any longer, and
launched his campaign with two tickets to the Coliseum, obviously designed to endear himself
to her. And guess what, she fell for it hook, line and sinker! Then he dumped her too!"

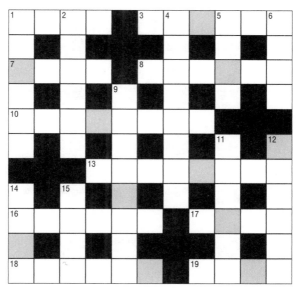

ACROSS

1 Something that needed clarification (4)

3 He was behaving like a hand-washing person (6)

7 See **17A** (4)

8 Alice was taken in by his air of sophistication (6)

10 He spun a **6D** after a detailed examination (8)

13 Noel had tickets for this venue (8)

16 He was an awkward oaf (6)

17 A glass or two of this, and a fatherly game of **7A** (4)

18 The type of desire Noel was showing (6)

19 He liked to lure young girls back here (4)

DOWN

1 Noel tried to be like someone glamorous from this TV show (6)

2 The tickets were designed to ingratiate himself to April (6)

4 After downing this Hope was in his arms (8)

5 Hope was eager to locate her boyfriend (4)

6 See **10A** (4)

9 After a brief summary of events (8)

11 The hat Noel wore (6)

12 What was **4D** designed to do to Hope's judgement (6)

14 These things leave a mark for life (4)

15 He was unable to stop himself any longer (4)

A Hairy Tale

At the Snips Hair Salon, the body of Dick Tate, manager, has been found brutally murdered. As Superintendent U. Sless is still under the drier, it is up to you, his loyal assistant, to catch the culprit.

EWAN MEE

"Ooh, how simply awful," cried Ewan. "Whatever shall we do without our Dick. He ran this place like clockwork. He was a true impresario and stage-managed everything perfectly!" Had he any idea who had killed the manager? "Just like a Mickey Spillane novel," he gushed. "Well, really, I think it was the handyman who did it. Built like the Colossus of Rhodes, he is. I can see him down on the farm, rough hands in the loam, urging on his team of Clydesdale horses. I offered him a manicure yesterday and he told me to clear off! Always ogling the customers and Dick wasn't very happy with that! Told him so too! And he caught him drinking whisky! He did it, he's got a nasty temper!"

STAN IMMER

"Meow, went the little cat," laughed Stan. "He's got a nerve—didn't like the brush off, did he?" Had he any idea who might have tried to brush off Dick, permanently? "Sure, the owner, Serge O'Drenalin. He didn't like his manager much—too much competition. Both with the bodies of athletes, both good looking, one with the brains of Einstein, and Serge with none! Unfortunately, having nothing else to recommend about him, he isn't exactly a draw card for the ladies' attention! Get rid of your rivals—that's his motto! And he did!"

SERGE O'DRENALIN

"What lies," declared Serge. "Stan is a good handyman—repaired all that was asked of him, and prompt, too—but a lousy detective." In that case, did he know who did the killing. "If you ask me, it's that little wimp, Ewan. Started to bawl like a baby when Dick burnt his prized mohair sweater on the curling iron and demanded compensation! Threw a tantrum when refused. If I had my way, I'd blast him off to the furthest asteroid I could find. That would keep him out of mischief!"

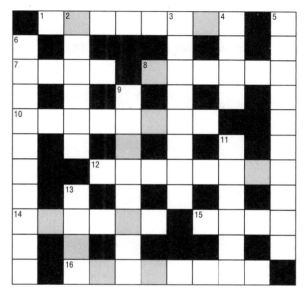

31

ACROSS

1 Just like a novel by Mickey — (8)
7 The little cat's sound (4)
8 What Stan was caught drinking (6)
10 He mended all that was asked of him (8)
12 Serge would blast Ewan to the furthest one (8)
14 Stan is built like the Colossus of where (6)
15 Ewan started to cry like a baby (4)
16 What Ewan offered the handyman (8)

DOWN

2 Stan was always on time (6)
3 They had bodies like these (8)
4 What Serge had nothing of to recommend (4)
5 These horses would need a lot of urging (10)
6 Dick was a true one, a born showman (10)
9 Dick had the brains of this scientist (8)
11 A prized sweater was made of soft wool (6)
13 Where the rough hands were put (4)

32

Wanda Lonely as a Cloud

The body of Wanda Dance has been found poisoned in the garden of her uncle's country house, Chestnut Manor. As Superintendent U. Sless has once again lost his way it is up to you to catch the culprit and discover in what the poison was concealed.

NOAH DANCE

"My poor sister!" lamented Noah. "How awful." Any ideas who killed her? "I suspect it was my uncle. She mocked him over his love of motor racing. He's always talking about his vacation in Italy last year—he went to Monza to see his hero, Jean Alesi, in the Grand Prix. He thought she was mad—he found her playing her cello to the birds in the aviary a few times. When he remonstrated she tried to stab him through the aorta with her bow! She was a real drama queen, forever quoting *Jane Eyre*. He wanted her committed!"

OTTO MOBEEL

"Completely false!" snorted Otto. "I didn't kill my niece." Did he know who had? "I believe it could have been Cristal next door. Since she moved here from Lyme Regis, they've had a spasmodic friendship. Cristal had her eye on my nephew and Wanda didn't like that. They had a falling out over it and Wanda chased her down the avenue and tried to strangle her with her parka! Cristal was rather scared of her, to say the least!"

CRISTAL GAYSER

"That's untrue!" exclaimed Cristal. "I didn't do it!" Did she have any clues who did kill her? "Noah, I think. She was an embarrassment to him and they were always at odds with each other. He saw her doing aerobics once, in Hyde Park in London—only problem was, she was in the buff. He roared about that for days. Some people never learn to behave properly and the whole family are as mad as each other—a folly to cross any of them!"

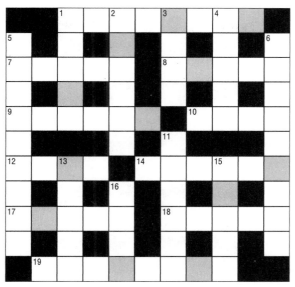

ACROSS

1 The type of exercise Wanda was doing (8)

7 What garment Wanda tried to strangle Cristal with (5)

8 It was stupid to cross any of them (5)

9 Cristal was frightened of Wanda (6)

10 This unspecified number of people never learn (4)

12 Noah and Wanda were always at loggerheads with each other (4)

14 The sort of road Cristal was chased down (6)

17 Otto's vacation destination last year (5)

18 His racing hero (5)

19 The novel Wanda was forever quoting (4, 4)

DOWN

1 Wanda tried to stab Otto through this (5)

2 Noah laughed for days over her exercise session (6)

3 She was in the nude when she did it (4)

4 The instrument Wanda played (5)

5 The type of friendship the two women had (9)

6 Where Cristal came from (4, 5)

11 Where the instrument was played (6)

13 Wanda was an over-the-top queen (5)

15 Wanda was this sort of relation to Otto (5)

16 The name of the London park (4)

Musical Murders

The body of Meg Awatt has been found in the public gardens of Blattley Village, brutally murdered. As Superintendent U. Sless is having trouble finding the right gate, it is up to you to solve the crime.

MICKY FINN

"Such a shock!" exclaimed Micky. "Finding her in the kids play area, dumped in the pirate's galleon!" Any ideas who did it? "Chris, the manager of entertainment is my bet. Meg was giving a series of piano recitals this summer, à la Dame Myra Hess. That's what the Pagoda Rotunda was built for. But she wanted a king's ransom. Chris hoards the entertainment money like a merchant refusing to part with a shekel more. He's altered the program so many times to suit her—I think he cracked!"

CHRIS CROSS

"Nonsense!" snorted Chris. "I think our warden has been on the job too long!" Any clues? "Les, the head gardener had a bone to pick with her. He found she had picked all his Madonna lilies; the only remnant was a few battered petals. He'd been nurturing them for weeks. Unfortunately his hound, Arthur, dug up the bulbs after her decimation and ate them. Then he found she'd been in the corral, where the deer are penned and left the gate open. Took him ages to lure them all back!"

LES HAPPY

"It certainly wasn't me!" cried Les. "What a pile of baloney!" In that case, who was it? "Micky, the bandleader, was in love with that stuck-up miss! She used to fill his head with dreams of how she would enrich their lives with the money she earned. She had a great hold over him. Then he found a letter from the oboe player, in her desk drawer, full of passionate references to a tryst they had a couple of nights ago. That was the factor that cracked that nut, and so he killed her!"

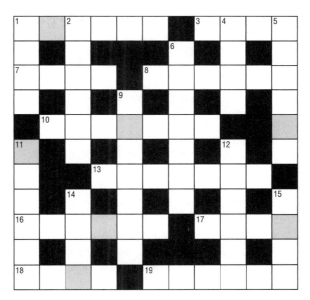

33

ACROSS

1 What cracked the nut (6)
3 Meg had a great power over Micky (4)
7 It took Les ages to entice the escaped animals back (4)
8 What was the rotunda called (6)
10 Meg's body was found dumped in the pirate's ship (7)
13 A few battered petals was the only bit left (7)
16 Refusing to part with a coin (6)
17 A heap of baloney (4)
18 Meg was a stuck-up woman (4)
19 What was the hound called (6)

DOWN

1 She used to stuff Micky's head with dreams (4)
2 A pen for the animals (6)
4 The player of this instrument had a tryst with Meg (4)
5 The letter was found in this part of the desk (6)
6 The lilies that were decimated (7)
9 Chris has changed the program so many times (7)
11 Meg wanted a king's what (6)
12 She was going to enhance their lives with the money she earned (6)
14 The surname of the pianist who Meg was going to emulate (4)
15 The animals that escaped (4)

Toil and Trouble

The body of Ian Trubble has been found brutally strangled in the Everyday Stores at Little Bicker Village. As Superintendent U. Sless has not yet completed his purchases, it is up to you to catch the culprit.

DAWN CHORUS

"Goodness!" cried Dawn. "What a shock finding Ian under the counter like that!" Did she know who had killed him? "It was Lex—he's hated Ian for years, ever since Ian has been able to thrash him at any sport they've played. He even won the ballroom dancing championships after Lex was sure he'd win. Ian was marrying his sister at All Souls Church on Saturday and Lex would have done anything to stop him. Now, instead of a bridal bouquet, she'll be carrying a funeral wreath!"

LEX ICON

"It certainly wasn't me!" snarled Lex, "although I must admit we didn't see eye to eye." Any idea who did kill him? "Ima has worked for him for years; he pays well so she must be in clover. But she is lazy and any exertion on her part calls for a lot of groaning. She's also clumsy—she dropped the carton of Tate & Lyle sugar, the packets split and ruined the special lamb order he'd got from the butcher! He thought she needed to be taught a lesson and gave her her marching orders on the spot!"

IMA GRUMP

"I didn't do it!" stormed Ima in a tart tone. "I was going to leave anyway—my husband's taking me on a long cruise down the River Elbe! And then we are joining an expedition to search for Atlantis!" In that case, who did do it? "Dawn's the one—she had agreed to take my job over but he made her swab the floors in the morning and then tried to impede her motley family from putting supplies on credit. When she protested that it would come out of her pay, he gave her a swat on the head which caused her to veer in an attempt to dodge it. Unfortunately, she knocked over a display and broke a lot of glass jars. He hit the roof and fired her!"

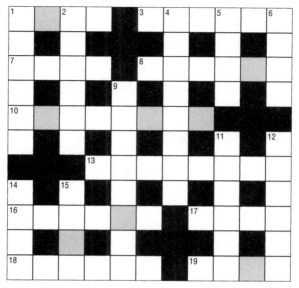

ACROSS

1 Ian made Dawn do this to the floors in the morning (4)

3 He thought she should be given a lesson (6)

7 Lex was certain that he'd win (4)

8 Ima must be in this, being paid so well (6)

10 Any effort on Ima's part calls for a lot of groaning (8)

13 Ian won these dancing championships (8)

16 The bride will be carrying this instead of a bouquet (6)

17 A cruise down which river (4)

18 Ian beat Lex at any sport (6)

19 The sugar was made by Tate & — (4)

DOWN

1 What relative of Lex was going to marry Ian (6)

2 Dawn had concurred to take over Ima's job (6)

4 The name of the church (3, 5)

5 Ian issued Ima her marching orders (4)

6 The type of tone Ima used (4)

9 The lost world Ima and her husband were going to search for (8)

11 Dawn's family were a varied bunch (6)

12 And Ian tried to stop them (6)

14 Ian gave Dawn this kind of blow on the head to Dawn (4)

15 Which caused her to turn in an attempt to dodge it (4)

Homely Horrors

The body of the matron, Honor Peddestal, has been found brutally battered in the basement of Sunset Towers Residential Home. As Superintendent U. Sless has inadvertently fallen over a wheelchair on the front steps it is up to you to catch the culprit.

MAY WURK

"Can't say I'm surprised," sniffed May. "She was terrible to work for—always in a ratty mood." Did she know who had killed her? "Yes, I'm sure it was Phyllis, she was so jealous of Honor. Honor was inclined to boast non-stop of her travels—trekking in Nepal, safari in the Congo, and visiting Inca ruins in Peru. All Phyllis gets each year is a week in Glamorgan. When we recently had a day trip to the seaside, she was so fed up with Honor, we saw her lunge forward and impel her off the jetty!"

PHYLLIS O'FICK

"What a tissue of lies!" exclaimed Phyllis. "I tripped, because Honor was trying to hustle us!" Any clues who killed her? "I think it was Cara. She loathed Honor. Claimed she belonged in the Jurassic. Once Honor found her in the staff bathroom, reading Aristotle! Cara claimed it was to improve her mind, but shut up like a clam when Honor cut through her pathetic excuses like a scythe. We all sent her a strong signal for that. We ignored her, and we're still not speaking to her!"

CARA LOTTE

"Totally undeserved, I might say!" retorted Cara. "I'm not the lazy one here!" Did she have any idea who had killed the matron. "May, without a doubt! She is a lasting monument to laziness! We have tried and tried to get her into a rhythm of work on a number of occasions but to no avail. And one of the residents accused her of trying to steal a tiara from amongst her belongings, and she stomped off in a huff, screaming bloody murder. She was going to be fired any day now!"

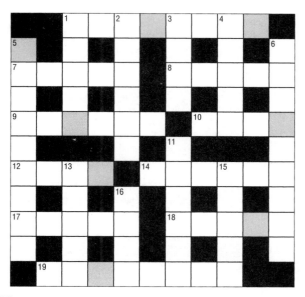

ACROSS

1 The era Honor belonged to (8)
7 The sort of mood she was always in (5)
8 She went trekking in this country (5)
9 Cara's excuses were cut through as if with this tool (6)
10 Cara shut up like this shellfish (4)
12 A single time, as Cara was found, in the staff bathroom (4)
14 More than a few occasions (6)
17 Phyllis took this step forward (5)
18 May was accused of trying to steal this (5)
19 A lasting edifice to laziness (8)

DOWN

1 What Honor was pushed off, at the seaside (5)
2 May couldn't get into this for her work (6)
3 How a signal was conveyed to Cara (4)
4 Push, as Phyllis did (5)
5 The author of the book Cara was reading (9)
6 Where Phyllis has her vacation (9)
11 Phyllis tripped, as Honor was trying to do this to them (6)
13 Where the safari was (5)
15 Honor was inclined to do this non-stop (5)
16 The country where the Inca ruins were (4)

Love's Labors Lost

The brutally murdered body of Gerry Canne has been found in the cellar at the Crippled Cock Bar. As Superintendent U. Sless is propping up the bar, it is up to you to catch the crook.

PHIL ANDERER

"Poor guy!" exclaimed Phil. "He was a top gun in the Air Force, but was dishonorably discharged—went crazy one day and turned his cannon on the ground crew!" Any idea who killed him? "Bart would be my guess. His heart would ache for Claire, the barmaid, and he and Gerry were deadly rivals for her affections. One day she'd be smooching under the vine with Gerry, and the next going for long walks in the dusk with Bart!"

BART ENDER

"Stuff and nonsense!" sputtered Bart. "I didn't do it!" Did he know who did then? "Maisy, the landlady, has uttered threats about him in the past. He walked into the kitchen one day when she was in the old zinc bathtub and poured a vat of lentil soup over her! She chased him with a palette knife, but slipped on the soap, fell back in the tub with a plop, and threw her back out! Even the people in the bar could hear the clatter and clash as those two went at it tooth and nail!"

MAISY DOATS

"Well, I never!" stated Maisy. "It certainly wasn't me!" In that case who was it? "I think Phil is the likeliest candidate! He used to work with UNICEF but ran off with his secretary to Assisi in Italy! He bumped into Gerry there, who took his love away from him. He's had a bias against Gerry ever since, and he is not the type to let things lie. He tried to frame Gerry—planted a lovely oval cut diamond in his pocket—but Gerry outwitted him with the neatest sleight of hand I've ever seen! Phil has been vowing vengeance since!"

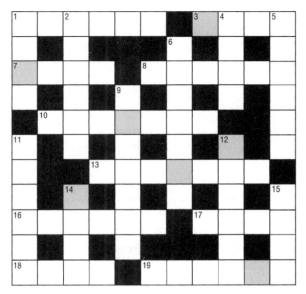

ACROSS

1 Gerry's post in the Air Force (3, 3)
3 The cut of the gem (4)
7 Maisy fell back in the tub with this (4)
8 Gerry went crazy one day and turned this weapon on the crew (6)
10 Noise heard in the bar (7)
13 A tidy sort of sleight of hand (7)
16 The organization Phil used to work for (6)
17 What the old bathtub was made of (4)
18 Long walks with Bart at what time (4)
19 The barmaid's name (6)

DOWN

1 Phil is not the sort to let things lie (4)
2 Even the folk in the bar could hear (6)
4 & **19A** and Gerry would smooch under it (4)
5 The spilt soup (6)
6 The sort of knife Maisy chased Gerry with (7)
9 The landlady has spoken threats about him in the past (7)
11 The crew Gerry aimed at (6)
12 Where in Italy Phil ran off to (6)
14 Phil has had this against Gerry ever since (4)
15 What Gerry felt in his heart for Claire (4)

Poetic Justice

The brutally strangled body of Brad All has been found in his bedroom in the village of Lower Slaughter. As Superintendent U. Sless has for some strange reason gone to the bathroom, it is up to you to conduct the investigation.

AL BRIGHT

"What a dreadful disappointment!" exclaimed Al. "Who would take his life? He was looking forward to giving a poetry reading on Ezra Pound's work at the Lyceum next week." Any idea who killed him? "Ivor would be my choice. They had a bitter argument about this recital—he thought it should be held at the Town Hall and wanted to do the reading himself. He was full of envy and was so rude to Brad. We will have to drum him out of the Poetry Appreciation Society!"

IVOR RACKET

"Nonsense!" snorted Ivor. "He was a great man and deserved this honor—why, he actually wept when he heard he was to do it!" Did he know who the killer was? "My guess would be Miles. He caused mayhem at the last reading, which was of some wonderful sacred books. He said holy offerings were no longer à la mode! He was incredibly impolite and called Brad an antiquated clod."

MILES TOGO

"I most certainly did not do it!" asserted Miles. "Brad was a good friend and client of myself and my business partner, Ronnie. We would do anything to oblige the chap." Who did he think killed him? "Personally, I think it was Al. He's been yearning to do the readings himself. He called Brad an old goat and told him he should be tossed in a ravine to rot! Claimed he couldn't get through a single page without having a catnap. All this back-biting was beginning to take its toll on Brad."

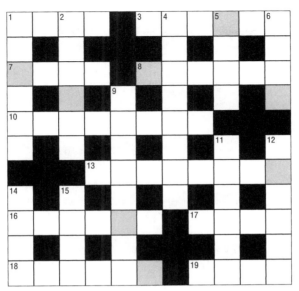

ACROSS

1 Brad's an antiquated one (4)
3 Where was Brad giving his poetry reading (6)
7 The back-biting was beginning.to take its what on Brad (4)
8 The last reading featured wonderful types of these books (6)
10 Brad and Ivor had a bitter one (8)
13 Ivor thought the recital should be held where (4, 4)
16 Miles' business partner (6)
17 Who would take Brad's existence? (4)
18 Miles caused this at the last reading (6)
19 Brad did this when he heard he was to do the reading (4)

DOWN

1 Al claimed Brad needed a what after reading a single page (6)
2 Miles and **16A** would to anything to please Brad (6)
4 Al had a desire to do the readings himself (8)
5 The forename of the poet (4)
6 Holy offerings are no longer à la — (4)
9 Miles was what to Brad (8)
11 Brad should be tossed in a crevice to rot (6)
12 Brad was not only a good friend but a customer as well (6)
14 Al wants to drive Ivor out of the society (4)
15 Ivor was full of jealousy (4)

Sea Shambles

Captain Fisheye has been found murdered in the bilges of his boat. Superintendent U. Sless, who gets seasick, is propping up the bar at the Mudway Yacht Club, so you have been rowed out to the scene of the crime.

ORRIN HANDS

"Ahoy, I'm the first mate, beware the boom as you come aboard," roared Orrin. "Dreadful voyage, my first in a tall ship and it ends in murder." Any clues as to who did it? "My guess is Walter—we sprung a leak in the last gale and although all the crew took turns, he was the one who spent the longest in the bilges pumping out. Diligent in his work, but the rough motion got to him and he flipped his lid!"

WALTER BAILER

"No, I didn't kill the Cap'n," said Walter. "He was the only one who would employ me. He was a great man. During storms he'd encourage us all to sing along to The Beatles, and we'd all be filled with optimism." Did he have any idea who the murderer was? "I reckon it was Al. We always get a rough assortment, but this one is worse than most. He tried to wring the neck of Omnivore, the ship's parrot, so-called because he ate anything and everything—and the Captain threatened to throw him overboard in the Bay of Biscay!"

AL ATSEA

"How dare that little twerp allege that I killed the Captain," snarled Al. "Plenty would have liked the chance. All Walter can see is what a good cosmetic job he's done on this boat—ornate figurehead, makes some feel like they're sailing the queen of the seas! And Captain Fisheye acting like some Elizabethan dandy, flicking his little epee in front of a full length mirror." Alright, then, who killed the Captain? "The first mate, of course. Always asking for more money, but old Fisheye, like Ebenezer Scrooge, wasn't about to part with any. Orrin wasn't too happy and that's an understatement!"

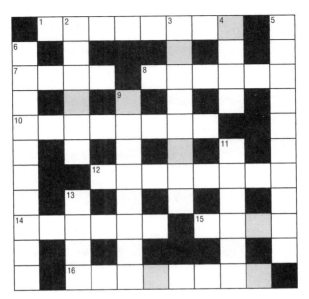

38

ACROSS

1 The surface job done by the Captain (8)

7 Captain would encourage them to be musical (4)

8 That little twerp made a claim that it was Al (6)

10 On the boat they were all filled with a positive attitude (8)

12 Walter was hard-working (8)

14 The Captain was the only one who would give Walter a job (6)

15 They sprung a leak in the last high wind (4)

16 The first name of the Dickensian character the Captain was likened to (8)

DOWN

2 The figurehead was fancy (6)

3 The sort of boat they were sailing (4, 4)

4 All of these took a turn pumping out (4)

5 The musical group they all joined in with during storms (3, 7)

6 They always got a rough kind of mixture (10)

9 The parrot's name (8)

11 Avoid the boom (6)

13 The Captain liked flicking this in front of a mirror (4)

Legionnaire's Demise

The body of Grant Peace has been found brutally murdered in the local American Legion bar. Superintendent U. Sless has inadvertently become entangled in the rose bush by the front door so it is up to you to unravel the crime.

ED OVERILLS

"Poor old fellow," lamented Ed. "We were great friends." Any ideas who did it? "Yes—Stan. Those two have been rivals ever since the war. They both served in the Navy, each on a corvette—Grant on *Idaho* and Stan on *Isis*. They seem to have emulated each other throughout their lives. You could almost merge them into one. The crunch came when Grant became betrothed to Molly, who works in the Naafi canteen, over his chicken kiev. Stan choked on his turbot—he wanted her for himself!"

STAN DATEASE

"What rubbish," snorted Stan. "He can't blame me for Grant's death!" Who did kill him then? "I think it might be Andy. He's completely ga-ga now—sits all day watching repeats of *The Muppet Show*. We thought it was just a phase he was going through but he's heading all-out towards senility. He got very impatient with Grant when he tried to stop him. His temper just gets worse."

ANDY MANN

"No, not true," exclaimed Andy. "I'm not ga-ga and I didn't do it!" Any clue who did then? "I know it was Ed. He's built like a shire horse and is as dashing as Errol Flynn. He was in the marines and thinks he was one of the elite. A useful fellow to have in a scrap. With him watching your rear you know you'll be okay! But he's been trying to enroll Grant in various nefarious goings on and he wasn't having that! He also tried to get Molly for himself—and that made him very unpopular with Grant and Stan. He didn't like the cold shoulder treatment he was getting, and it made him very, very angry!"

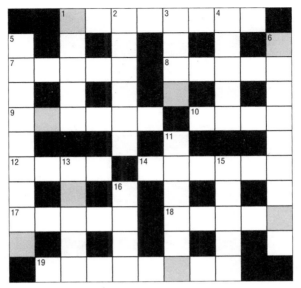

39

ACROSS

1 They seem to have equaled each other all their lives (8)

7 You could almost join them to make them one (5)

8 Ed was built like this type of horse (5)

9 He's heading resolutely towards senility (3-3)

10 With Ed watching this part of you, you know you are okay (4)

12 Stan served on a boat called this (4)

14 Andy watches this show (6)

17 Where Molly works (5)

18 You can't condemn Stan for Grant's death (5)

19 The warship they served on (8)

DOWN

1 Ed was dashing, like Flynn (5)

2 A handy fellow (6)

3 Ed tried to get Molly for himself as well (4)

4 Ed thinks he was one of this group (5)

5 Andy got very agitated with Grant when he tried to stop him (9)

6 Grant became engaged to Molly (9)

11 The fish Stan choked on (6)

13 Grant served on a boat called this (5)

15 They thought it was just a stage Andy was going through (5)

16 Grant's chicken dish (4)

Hostel Hostility

The body of May Flower has been found murdered in the kitchen of the Little Bicker Youth Hostel. As Superintendent U. Sless is busy sampling the fare on offer it is up to you to solve the crime.

DOT COMM

"It's no surprise," stated Dot. "She wasn't a very nice girl." Any idea who did it then? "May was always picking on Sally, who made the mistake of confiding in her. May loved to see her squirm as she was about to expose something Sally had just told her. Sally had a gift for horses and her latest ambition, as revealed by May, was to become an equerry at the Royal Stables! May said they'd reject her as soon as they saw her! Poor Sally, she was so upset, she attacked May with the skillet!"

SALLY ALLY

"It's true I didn't like May!" agreed Sally. "But I didn't kill her!" Did she know who did then? "Everybody had a grudge against her, but I think Honey could be the type to sink to murder! First of all, she wanted to be a model like Tyra Banks but was unlike any model you've ever seen. May made her writhe by telling everyone! Said she was a manipulative user and more like a limpet than a supermodel and Honey's eyes just flooded with tears. May was a nasty piece of work and definitely due for a fall."

HONEY BEE

"Oh, no!" cried Honey. "I didn't do it!" Who did then? "Dot is the sort to nourish ill-feeling. She belongs to the local unit of the ASPCA and had asked May to assist in some sort of meeting they were having at Easter. Unfortunately, May took her Skye terrier with her, which ran amok and frightened off some of the nesting birds! In the lull that followed Dot was heard to clearly threaten to get even with May and judging by the look on her face, she meant it!"

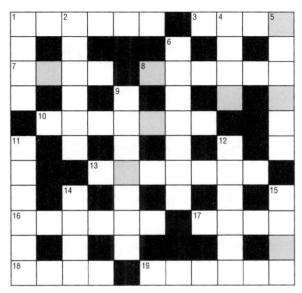

40

ACROSS

1 Everybody had an aversion to May (6)

3 Dot was clearly heard to threaten May in the calm that followed (4)

7 May was due for this (4)

8 May loved to see Sally ill-at-ease (6)

10 Sally attacked May with what (7)

13 Dot is the sort to foster ill-feeling (7)

16 When was the meeting (6)

17 Honey is the type to descend to murder (4)

18 Honey wanted to be like this model (4)

19 May made Honey twitch by telling everyone (6)

DOWN

1 Sally had a talent for animals (4)

2 Honey was different from any model you've ever seen (6)

4 Dot belongs to a local what of the ASPCA (4)

5 Honey was more like this mollusk than a model (6)

6 Sally's latest ambition was to work with the Queen's horses (7)

9 Her eyes brimmed over with tears (7)

11 May said they'd turn Sally down as soon as they saw her (6)

12 Dot asked May to help at a meeting (6)

14 She was also a conniver (4)

15 The terrier that ran amok (4)

41

Scarlett Fever

The badly beaten body of Scarlett Bean has been found in the local church of the village of Much Muckle. As Superintendent U. Sless has become stuck on his knees after genuflecting, it is up to you to apprehend the murderer.

HARRY BEAN

"My poor wife!" cried Harry. "She was a bit of a prankster and made a few enemies!" Any idea which one killed her? "Dai is my bet. His uncle is a Bishop, and came to give the reading at the funeral of Dai's mother. Scarlett had applied super glue to the bier and the reverend unfortunately rested his hands on it—and stuck fast. Dai looked like Popeye, with his eyes bulging out of their sockets—he was ready to flip! He chased her out of the church, trying to whack her with an old lyre!"

DAI LAFFING

"Certainly wasn't me!" exclaimed Dai. "But I was very upset about what she did to Uncle Willis, him being a respectable man of God!" In that case, did he know who did kill her? "I think Monty did it. Scarlett had an honest face and could sell sand in the desert. Monty was experiencing problems with his voice—a wonderful rich baritone. She told him it would be enhanced by gargling with genuine water from the River Liffey. Unfortunately, it was neat olive oil, which made him start choking. He had to spend a week at the Roache Clinic to recover!"

MONTY CLIMBER

"Well, it wasn't me!" snorted Monty. "Although I had good reason—I was about to cut a demo tape but missed out, because of her!" Who did he think was the culprit? "I think Harry did it. Poor old guy, I wouldn't swap my life for his. He used to be such a jovial fellow, bit of flab around the middle. Then Scarlett decided he was too fat and issued a decree he was to diet. He was virtually just an echo of his former self. I think it pushed him to the edge of insanity!"

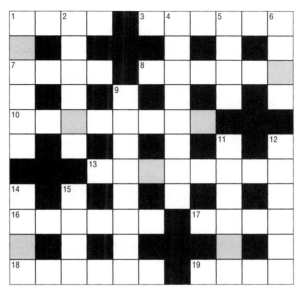

ACROSS

1 Dai was trying to whack Scarlett with this old instrument (4)
3 She had a face of probity (6)
7 Harry had a bit of this around the middle (4)
8 Dai's uncle was a clergyman (6)
10 Scarlett told Monty his voice would be improved by gargling (8)
13 His voice was a wonderful rich pitch (8)
16 The uncle's name (6)
17 The frame he rested his hands on (4)
18 Dai resembled this cartoon character (6)
19 The **17A** had this super adhesive on it (4)

DOWN

1 Genuine water from which river (6)
2 Monty's clinic (6)
4 What he gargled with (5, 3)
5 Harry was just a reflection of his former self (4)
6 Monty had been about to cut a demo cassette (4)
9 The diet pushed Harry to the edge of madness (8)
11 He used to be such a happy fellow (6)
12 Scarlett issued an edict (6)
14 Monty wouldn't change his life (4)
15 Dai was ready to go berserk in church (4)

Herbal Remedy

Chef Herb Grower has been found strangled at the exclusive Last Supper Restaurant. Superintendent U. Sless is examining the hors d'oeuvres so you must go to the kitchen and interview the suspects.

NOEL TRUBBLE

"Wow, fancy somebody taking on old Herb," laughed Noel. "He was a regular martinet and domineered us all magnificently!" Did he have any idea who might not have taken too kindly to this? "Look no further than Manuel," responded Noel readily. "He's an asylum seeker from some godforsaken country and an absolute clown! Stick him on an electric tricycle with a tassel on his backside and shove him in a three-ring circus. He'd be a roaring success! He was terrified of Herb, who was always making a fuss about him dropping utensils and breaking crockery."

MANUEL WORKER

"I didn't do it!" cried Manuel. "I don't kill kind people who give me a job!" Did he have any idea at all who could have then? "I don't like to tell tales," replied Manuel, "but Dinah has a lot of problems with the chef. She had an instinct he meant her some sort of harm so she always made herself scarce. He thought he was a great stud, and he tried to kiss her, and she pushed him away! She was shaking with anger afterwards."

DINAH LONE

"No, I didn't do it, although I felt like it," admitted Dinah. In that case, did she have any clues as to who could have? "Yes, indeed! Noel is a rotten piece of work! He was always dropping his dentures into the Brie for a laugh and sold the sturgeon Herb was preparing for a special dinner tonight—Herb went ballistic and was ready to fire him. He's the one who did it!"

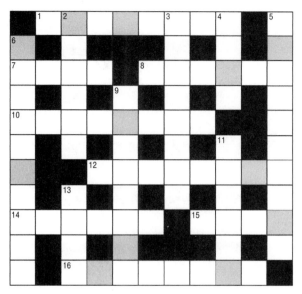

42

ACROSS

1 Manuel was always dropping implements (8)
7 ...and the chef was always making a song and dance about it (4)
8 Manuel was seeking this (6)
10 & **12A** Vehicle Manuel should ride (8)
12 See **10A** (8)
14 Noel is this piece of work (6)
15 What was the cheese (4)
16 What was always dropped in the cheese for a laugh (8)

DOWN

2 Noel would have liked to have seen this on Manuel's backside (6)
3 Dinah has this about the chef (8)
4 The fish was traded (4)
5 The chef lorded over everybody magnificently (10)
6 Dinah was shaking with anger later (10)
9 What type of fish was it (8)
11 Dinah always tried to make herself hard to find (6)
13 The chef thought he was a great casanova (4)

43

A Fishy Finale

The badly lacerated body of Rod Castor has been found lying behind the brambles beside the stream at the village of Sprat's Bottom. Superintendent U. Sless has unfortunately fallen into the stream so it is once again up to you to solve the crime.

IVOR TIDDLER

"Dreadful doings," exclaimed Ivor. "Our fishing club is going to miss Rod." Did he know who had killed him? "Rocky seems a likely choice. He's got the temper and the strength. He's a fan of the boxer Frank Bruno, and is interested in any boxing promotion going. He accidentally caught an otter the other day and Rod hit the roof and heaped abuse on his head. Rocky threw a plank at him in rage!"

ROCKY SHAW

"He's a great one to tattle!" snorted Rocky. "I didn't do it." Did he know who did then? "Yes, it was Chip. Rod was our top fisherman and caught a record huss recently when he went deep-sea fishing. Up till then, Chip had a slim chance of winning the annual prize, which involves a tidy sum and a night in town at a film premiere. A relation of his is having money problems and he wanted the cash desperately to enable him to help out. Rod had ruined that plan—he ruled the roost when it came to catching record-breakers!"

CHIP BUTTY

"What an infamous lie," cried Chip. "He should be made to scour his mouth out!" Any ideas who the culprit is then? "Yes indeed. It was Ivor. He isn't as prim and proper as he would have you believe. He is no choir boy, goes to the premiere of every horror movie, and likes to roast the fish we catch. We are in constant fear of a spot check and have to hide his grim activities to deter any copycats and keep our reputation intact. Rod was all for kicking him out, and that is why Ivor killed him!"

ACROSS

1 A member of Chip's family (8)
7 What Rocky threw in rage (5)
8 They had to do this to any copycats (5)
9 Ivor is a great one to gossip (6)
10 Ivor isn't as upright and proper as he would have you believe (4)
12 The fish caught when Rod went deep-sea fishing (4)
14 They wanted to keep their reputation in one piece (6)
17 Ivor isn't what kind of boy (5)
18 The surname of the famous boxer Rocky is a fan of (5)
19 Ivor goes to the first night of every horror movie (8)

DOWN

1 Rod likes to bake the fish (5)
2 Rocky seems a fitting choice (6)
3 The prize money was a neat sum (4)
4 The accidental catch (5)
5 They are in constant fear of a what (4, 5)
6 Rocky was interested in any boxing championship (9)
11 Winning the prize money would let Chip help out (6)
13 Rocky should be made to clean his mouth out (5)
15 Rod heaped invective on Rocky's head (5)
16 They have to hide his cruel activities (4)

Last Rites

The body of Bill O'Rites has been found brutally murdered in the lounge at Much Muckle Salvation Army Hostel. As Superintendent U. Sless is busy learning to play the tambourine it is up to you to catch the culprit.

MORTY FIED

"Poor old fellow!" exclaimed Morty. "What a way to go!" Any idea who did it? "I suspect it was Will, he's a bit of an odd bird. Always wearing flared pants and that dreadful purple kaftan that's a relic of the sixties! Bill had accused him of stealing an old watch his grandfather Albert had given him. Will swore an oath that the accusation was an offense that would not be forgotten!"

WILL FULL

"Ha, silly old fool!" jeered Will. "I didn't do it!" Who did then? "That Archie is an evil old coot! He's got a temper to match Attila the Hun. When he'd found that Bill had borrowed his book about Mercia, he belted him over the head with a piccolo he'd stolen from the church! Bill was in a terrible dither over it, he started to cry in the middle of a hymn at Evensong. Once his tears flowed, you could just about keep the entire fleet afloat!"

ARCHIE BUNCLE

"Lies!" growled Archie. "It wasn't me!" Any clues then? "Yeah, Morty isn't as white as he paints himself. He was always causing poor old Bill anxiety. He has a heart of iron, and nothing can bend it. Bill made a blunder by telling Will that Morty has a secret cavity under the floorboards. Morty was very incensed that his hiding-place had been exposed and Bill lost a valuable ally!"

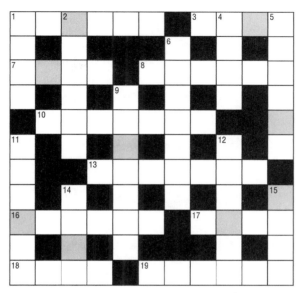

44

ACROSS

1 Will was always wearing these trousers (6)
3 Will's an odd one (4)
7 He swore a pledge (4)
8 Bill could just about keep the entire fleet sailing with his tears (6)
10 Bill made this mistake (7)
13 The musical instrument stolen from the church (7)
16 Morty had a secret what under the floorboards (6)
17 Morty was extremely incensed (4)
18 Bill lost a valuable friend (4)
19 This item of clothing was a relic from the sixties (6)

DOWN

1 Once Bill's tears started to run (4)
2 Archie has a temper to match this Hun (6)
4 Morty's heart was this metal (4)
5 Bill got into this terrible state (6)
6 The accusation was a crime that wouldn't be forgotten (7)
9 Morty was always causing Bill stress (7)
11 The borrowed book was about a part of Anglo-Saxon England (6)
12 Bill's grandfather (6)
14 Archie was this kind of old coot (4)
15 Bill started to cry in the middle of this song (4)

Pilot Error

The badly battered body of Rod Barron has been found behind a hangar at the Pleasant Pastures Airfield. As Superintendent U. Sless is terrified of flying, it is up to you to carry out the investigation.

STAN DOVER

"Best pilot I've got!" exclaimed Stan. "He was a real daredevil though." Who did he think had killed him? "I think it was Darryl—he's a great mechanic and fusses over the planes as if they were his own! Nobody but Rod would dare to do dumb stunts. Darryl imagined he was going to bust up the planes. He was fierce in his protection of them. It was an ordeal for him to watch Rod's aerobatics—he would just about keel over in horror. Rod was a show-off, his antics were designed to stun and that gave Darryl a good enough reason to kill him!"

DARRYL SPANNER

"It wasn't me!" stated Darryl. "Sure, I hated the way he treated the planes but he was a talented flyer! I believe he is an ex-Qantas pilot." Did he know who it was then? "Must have been Rex. He was jealous of Rod's ability and wanted to be the ace here. A modest one, but filled with unholy glee when Rod was in trouble. Rex is a very trusty man in the air and his pre-flight preparations would be carried out as if they were a religious rite!"

REX ITALL

"It most certainly was not me!" snorted Rex. "I disliked Rod's rashness with the planes, but I wouldn't stoop to murder!" Who would then? "Stan has been steadily losing money, mainly through repair bills—caused by Rod's stunts. He was about to call in the Bankruptcy Receiver. Stan thought this business would evolve into a big money earner. We've only had sporadic business, mere short hops. Stan had hoped to draw crowds. It hasn't been easy on him and he cracked!"

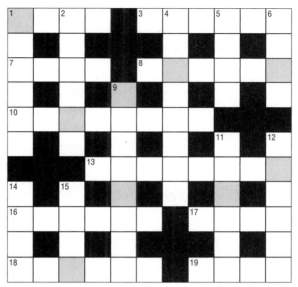

45

ACROSS

1 Only short hops (4)
3 Darryl was savage in his protection (6)
7 Stan had hoped to bring in the crowds (4)
8 The airline Rod used to fly for (6)
10 They'd only had irregular business (8)
13 Stan was about to call in an official (8)
16 Rex is a very what man in the air (6)
17 He would be filled with unholy happiness (4)
18 Anybody? No (6)
19 Darryl would fall over in horror (4)

DOWN

1 Rex was a humble chap (6)
2 A good enough motive to kill (6)
4 Darryl envisaged that Rod would bust up the planes (8)
5 Rex's pre-flight preparations were like a religious ceremony (4)
6 It hasn't been simple for Stan (4)
9 Darryl thought Rod was a gifted flyer (8)
11 Stan thought the business would turn into a money earner (6)
12 It was a trial for Darryl to watch Rod's aerobatics (6)
14 Rod's antics were designed to astound (4)
15 Rod was the only one who would dare to do stupid stunts (4)

Swift Justice

Superintendent U. Sless has been called to Great Dahlias, the country home of Captain Swift, where his broken body has been found in the formal rose garden. As our intrepid policeman has, by error, gone to Great Daisies, you will have to, once again, investigate the crime.

VERA SWIFT

"How dreadful," wailed Vera. "That someone could have killed such a brave man as my husband. He's traveled the world, dined with Glen Hoddle in Stalingrad, rounded Cape Horn several times, and sailed the Orient, collecting shrapnel in his shoulder from a brush with pirates! Now my beloved Jonathon is no more!" Did she have any idea who killed him? "Oh, indeed I do!" she exclaimed. "That no good son of mine, he hated his father and wanted him out of the way! He wanted his hands on the estate and would have done anything to get it!"

IAN SWIFT

"My dear mother is distraught, I fear," responded Ian dryly. "An unlikely trio of suspects you seem to have rounded up." And was one of them the killer? "I would be very much inclined to believe it was the gardener, Doug O'Ver, whom my father brought back with him from his travels in County Antrim. A black-hearted soul who would willingly take Nero as his idol. Father found him in the greenhouse, suffering from a hangover— any excuse to malinger—and threatened to send him back where he came from, imminently!"

DOUG O'VER

"I wouldn't have ever hurt the Captain," whined Doug. "He's been good to me for years and rescued me from a life of poverty!" Did he have any clue as to who did it? "That simpering wife of his," he growled. "Led him a dog's life when he was at home! Not an atom of kindness in her! Refused to serve him luncheon because he was too rotund! But she didn't like him going off on his travels and found a way to keep him put, permanently!"

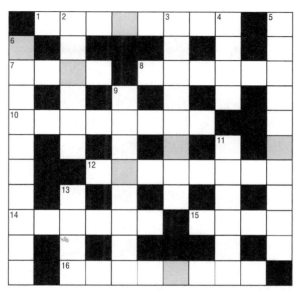

ACROSS

1 The first name of Vera's beloved (8)
7 An unlikely what of suspects (4)
8 The gardener's home county (6)
10 Vera wouldn't serve the Captain a meal (8)
12 A place he rounded several times (4, 4)
14 She refused to serve food because the Captain was too... (6)
15 **4D** was Doug's hero (4)
16 He would use any excuse to loiter (8)

DOWN

2 Where the Captain sailed (6)
3 The gardener suffered from too much drink the night before (8)
4 See **15A** (4)
5 The Captain threatened to send Doug back where he came from soon (10)
6 The city where the Captain dined (10)
9 What he collected in his shoulder (8)
11 The surname of the person with whom the Captain dined (6)
13 Vera didn't have one iota of kindness in her (4)

A Fitting End

The body of Deb O'Naire has been found in a fitting room in Fine Things Department Store. As Superintendent U. Sless has been constricted in the corsetry department, it is up to you to solve the crime.

DEE BATES

"How dreadful!" exclaimed Dee. "In all my years as a retailer, I've never seen the like!" Did she know who had committed the crime? "Yes, Heather! Deb always asked that she fit her up for her travels—off to Cairo this year with her husband Ivor, and a boat trip down the River Nile. Heather tried to persuade her into a lacy dress in cyan, more suitable for a visit to the opera. Certainly not for Deb. Her star sign is Taurus, and I must admit, she suits it—built like a bull, with huge round biceps and a neigh that passes for a laugh! Heather made an enemy of her, and a dangerous one at that!"

HEATHER BELL

"Nonsense," stated Heather. "Mrs O'Naire and I have a relationship that doesn't waver, no matter what!" Did she have any ideas about the killer? "Yes, her so-called friend, Tara. They did a lot together—traveled to Swaziland last year, and spent Christmas in Zurich. But I believe Tara is jealous of her. Mrs O'Naire told me that when they were practicing Tai Chi, Tara, not once but thrice, fell against her, each time with a hearty thud, until she eventually fell over. Tara could have rivaled Roger Bannister the way she sprinted off!"

TARA MILLIONE

"Preposterous!" snorted Tara. "I'll have her fired!" In that case did she have any clue as to the killer? "The manageress, Dee, did it. She sold Deb a dress that made her look like a chute. She wanted something nice to wear to her daughter's debut performance in the woodwind section of the Philharmonic Orchestra, but she looked awful. Dee tried to pacify her but she was threatening to take her business elsewhere and that would have ruined this shop!"

ACROSS

1 Dee has spent all these years as a vendor (8)

7 The relationship between Deb and Heather didn't change (5)

8 Heather made a dress that was more suitable for a visit where (5)

9 Where Christmas was spent (6)

10 & **12A** The color and fabric of the dress made (4)

12 See **10A** (4)

14 Deb's star sign (6)

17 She had a laugh like a what (5)

18 Deb was sold a dress that made her look like a what (5)

19 The section of the orchestra for the daughter's debut (8)

DOWN

1 The Nile is one of these (5)

2 How many times did Tara fall against Deb (6)

3 Deb's husband (4)

4 Heather made a dangerous opponent (5)

5 Where the two ladies traveled to last year (9)

6 The athlete's surname (9)

11 What the two ladies were practising (3, 3)

13 Deb's off to which city with her husband (5)

15 The shape of Deb's biceps (5)

16 Tara fell against Deb with a hearty what (4)

48

Fatal Beauty

The strangled body of Annie Boyes has been found behind the stage at Pleasant Pastures Annual Beauty Pageant. As Superintendent U. Sless is busy admiring the line-up of beauties, it is up to you to apprehend the killer.

BELLA MOORE

"What a horrible thing to happen!" cried Bella. "But she was a very vain girl, and nobody liked her much!" Who did she think had killed her? "I am sure it was Emma. Annie thought she was the cat's pajamas, she had an overwhelming dose of egomania. She was boasting about some chic Duke she's been seeing and showed us a telegram he sent, inviting her to dine. She sent off her RSVP pretty quick. The only trouble is, Emma had been going out with him previously. She was really cut up!"

EMMA BRACE

"Nonsense, I didn't do it!" exclaimed Emma. "How dare she suggest it!" In that case who did? "Our chaperone, May, is a good bet. She runs this show as if it is a stalag! She's a moldy old fossil with an icicle for a heart. Annie gave her a nudge when we were out shopping and she fell headfirst into some wet cement. She was going to belt Annie but we managed to dilute the situation. Unfortunately, Annie then told her she should have run a prison in the old USSR!"

MAY MARRY

"It most certainly was not me!" sniffed May. "But that girl was a nasty piece of work. She could optimize any tense occasion to her own advantage." Who was the killer then? "I'm rather afraid it was Bella. She is a charming girl who tried to ease things. When Annie said her room was too noisy, Bella immediately said she would vacate hers for her. She gave her a large share of an eggplant casserole when Annie complained she wasn't getting enough to eat. The crunch came when Bella slipped and broke Annie's collection of Ella Fitzgerald records and received a deluge of abuse. The poor girl was in floods of tears!"

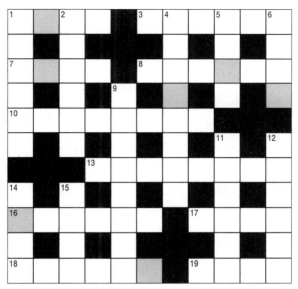

ACROSS

1 Annie was a very conceited girl (4)
3 Bella received a torrent of abuse (6)
7 The elegant Duke (4)
8 May is a moldy old relic (6)
10 How was the dinner invitation sent (8)
13 Annie could make the best of any tense occasion (8)
16 May ran the show as if it was a prison (6)
17 Annie was boasting about a titled gentleman (4)
18 She responded to his invitation very smartly (6)
19 May was going to hit Annie (4)

DOWN

1 Bella said she would move out of her room for Annie (6)
2 May had this for a heart (6)
4 Annie had an overwhelming dose of arrogance (8)
5 May should have run a prison in this former country (inits) (4)
6 The singer whose records were broken (4)
9 Bella's casserole ingredient (8)
11 The girls managed to tone down the situation (6)
12 May fell headfirst into this wet mixture (6)
14 Annie's invitation reply (initials) (4)
15 Bella tried to calm things (4)

Feeling Flat

The horribly mutilated body of Mike Impay, landlord, has been found on the third floor of his block of apartments on the East Side. Superintendent U. Sless is unfortunately trapped in the elevator between the first and second floors, so it is up to you, his trusted assistant, to find the murderer.

THEO LOGIAN

"Dreadful news about Mr. Impay!" exclaimed Theo. "I am studying for my bar exams but have been laid up with a tropical virus." Did he have any ideas about the killer? "I have my suspicions. Terry is a real bad apple, always causing trouble. He races around Smithfield Market on his motorcycle, frightening everyone. He's a tearaway and Mike had threatened him with eviction if he didn't mend his ways!"

TERRY WAY

"What a narrow minded little so-and-so that guy is," Terry laughed. "Only he could automatically equate motorbike with murder! He's got a gigantic chip on his shoulder." So, who did it then? "I reckon it was little Miss Mona Allott. She's a funny one! Reads Marx until three o'clock in the morning and then she will unfasten the front door and appear on the pavement, in the nude! Mike had given her notice, but she wasn't having that!"

MONA ALLOTT

"I've been sleepwalking!" explained Mona. "And Mike was very understanding about it!" Did she know who the culprit is? "Yes, it's that Theo. I don't wager a cent he'll pass his exams. He's too busy nosing around our business all the time. He implements a new rule and expects us all to dance to his tune. Mike told him he was the landlord and he wasn't having any of that nonsense, et cetera, and Theo didn't like that, one little bit!"

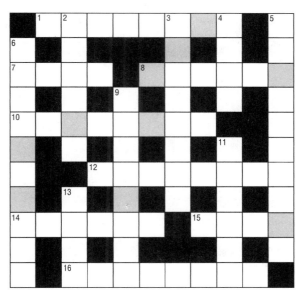

49

ACROSS

1 Mona will open the front door (8)

7 She is an avid reader of this writer (4)

8 Theo has been bedridden with **10A** (4, 2)

10 Theo's virus (8)

12 Terry is a real one of these (3, 5)

14 Theo will automatically link motorbike and murder (6)

15 The coin Mona wouldn't wager on Theo (4)

16 Mona wasn't having any of that nonsense, and the rest (2, 6)

DOWN

2 Theo's mind is not open (6)

3 Terry is a hooligan (8)

4 Mona stands on the pavement in the buff (4)

5 Theo brings in a new rule (10)

6 The market Terry races around (10)

9 Size of chip that Theo has (8)

11 Mona will materialize on the pavement (6)

13 Theo wants them all to dance to his... (4)

Loony Tunes

The brutally murdered body of Harvey Loon has been found in the duck pond at Little Bicker. As Superintendent U. Sless, is busy picking a bunch of daffodils to take home to his wife, it is up to you to solve the crime.

SYD DOWNE

" How awful!" exclaimed Syd. "He was a rascal, though." Any idea who killed him? "His buddy Cliff had cause. After being sent down from Oxford, Harvey borrowed Cliff's yacht and went cruising in the Aegean with friends. A pirate ship attacked them and the yacht sunk. They managed to cram into the Avon dinghy and jury-rigged a sail and the breeze carried them to Mykonos. After capsizing on the rocks they were able to wade ashore, although Harvey said it was like a slalom course, threading through the jagged edges. Anyway, the boat wasn't insured so Cliff is furious!"

CLIFF HANGER

"Really!" drawled Cliff. "It definitely wasn't me!" Who was it then? "Mona had to endure a lot from him. She was ready to ditch him. He and his friends burst into her boudoir the other night, drunk on kirsch, and hell-bent on mischief. They managed to break a very valuable enamel snuffbox of rare beauty. She was incensed, called him a rodent of the lowest kind, and kicked him out!"

MONA WAYE

"Well!" cried Mona. "I'm certainly not guilty." Who is then? "Syd's the one! They've been trouble-makers together for years and then Harvey began trying to exclude Syd. There has been a hint of desperation in Syd as he keeps trying to recycle the friendship. He needed to buck up and realize he'd been a pawn in Harvey's games. Trouble is, I think he went too far and killed him!"

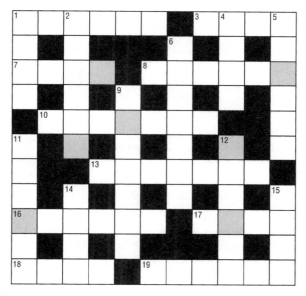

50

ACROSS

1 What carried them to **9D** (6)
3 They managed to paddle ashore (4)
7 They were able to squash into the dinghy (4)
8 Harvey was sent down from where (6)
10 Syd keeps trying to salvage the friendship (7)
13 Harvey and his friends burst into Mona's bedroom (7)
16 Threading through the rocks was like an obstacle course (6)
17 The snuffbox was of unusual beauty (4)
18 There has been a touch of desperation (4)
19 What Mona called Harvey (6)

DOWN

1 Syd needed to perk up (4)
2 What the snuffbox was made of (6)
4 The type of dinghy used (4)
5 Mona has had to put up with a lot from Harvey (6)
6 Harvey began trying to do this to Syd (7)
9 The Aegean island they were carried to (7)
11 What Harvey and his mates were drunk on (6)
12 Buccaneer ship that attacked them (6)
14 Syd had been a dupe in Harvey's games (4)
15 They were hell-what on mischief (4)

51

Museum Mystique

The brutally battered body of Sir Hugh Geego has been found in the storeroom of his annex. As Superintendent U. Sless has walked into the glass doors and knocked himself out, it is up to you to conduct the investigation.

AVERY BADUN

"He will be missed!" exclaimed Avery. "However, some will say it served him right!" Any clues to the killer? "Paddy is your probable culprit. Hugh has treated him like a serf ever since we made him curator of our museum. Hugh had set the exhibits up randomly, so Paddy got to work and did a superb job of sorting the displays out. Hugh, in an extremely nasty manner, went on to advise him not to exceed his authority. They got into a little tiff over it!"

PADDY WAGON

"It most certainly wasn't me!" stated Paddy. "I rather value my job too much." In that case, did he know who had done it? "Yes, indeed. Penny has been trying to ensnare him for ages. She learnt to hula dance in Honolulu and would undulate in front of him, waving glasses of asti at him, trying desperately to entice him! Big slip-up, she should have asked for a refund—he was a beer drinker. He told her to clear out and she threatened to bash him with a ceremonial mace from one of the displays!"

PENNY DROP

"What nerve!" stormed Penny. "I'm not a killer." Who is then? "Hugh's friend and partner—Avery. He's lost money in the stock market, and this place is richer than Fort Knox. There's the wonderful manuscript room, with originals from Sir Kingsley Amis, and his son Martin. Plus a valuable original from the Bard himself—Shakespeare. The Saturn Suite houses all those gorgeous relics Hugh brought back from Ankara. Unfortunately for Avery and all petty thieves, security is tighter than a drum. A mouse couldn't emit a squeak without setting the alarms off. So Avery had to resort to murder!"

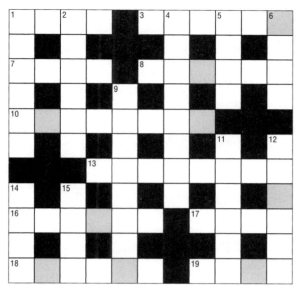

ACROSS

1 Hugh treated Paddy like a slave (4)
3 Paddy did a great job sorting out the displays (6)
7 Hugh and Paddy got into a little... (4)
8 In a nasty manner, Hugh went on to instruct him (6)
10 The exhibits were set out haphazardly by Hugh (8)
13 The place was richer than this gold depository (4, 4)
16 Hugh was the curator of it (6)
17 Penny tried to bash Hugh with a ceremonial one (4)
18 Penny made a big mistake (4-2)
19 There was a valuable original from Shakespeare himself (4)

DOWN

1 Relics were in this suite (6)
2 Penny should have got her money back (6)
4 Penny would wiggle in front of Hugh (8)
5 A mouse couldn't let out a squeak (4)
6 Hugh drank ale (4)
9 Where Penny learnt to hula dance (8)
11 Where the gorgeous relics came from (6)
12 Paddy was trying to go beyond his authority (6)
14 The father and son novelists (4)
15 Penny tried to entice Hugh with glasses of it(4)

A Stable Relationship

The badly battered body of Irma Boss has been found at the Jolly Jumper Stables. Superintendent U. Sless was last seen belting down the lane with a bad tempered Shetland pony after him, so it is up to you to solve the crime.

LOTTIE HAY

"Bad news about Irma," exclaimed Lottie. "I don't know what will happen here at the stables now." Does she have any clues as to who killed Irma? "I think it was probably Amie. She's got a streak of laziness in her and Irma was always telling her to be like her namesake, Amy Johnson, and fly around, instead of crawling around like a turtle! She was always hurting Amie's feelings and metaphorically tearing julienne strips off her morale!"

AMIE SLACKER

"I didn't kill her, though!" cried Amie. "I'm not like that!" Who is then? "Try Dandy for size—he thought he was in love with her. He'd sneak down to Atherton Hall, where she lived, and serenade her. She hated it and last time he did it she punched his nose, chased him off, and he fell into the pond and ruined her precious water iris!"

DANDY BRUSH

"She would have grown to love me in time," sniffed Dandy. Did he have any idea who killed her? "Yes, I do! Lottie did it. She is a sterling silver cow with an inborn capacity for trouble. Made out like she was good friends with Roy Marsden, the actor—that was a lie! Told Irma hand-painted livery was a thing of the past and tried to involve the three of us in a love triangle! Her mind was a tortuous mire and we didn't need that here, and Irma told her so. So Lottie killed her!"

52

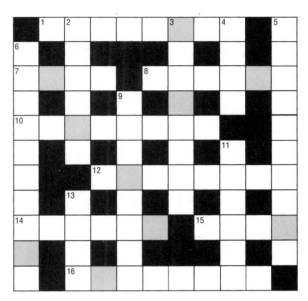

ACROSS

1 The name of the Hall (8)
7 Lottie's mind was a tortuous bog (4)
8 Hand-painted regalia is a thing of the past (6)
10 What were the metaphorical strips torn off Amie's morale (8)
12 Irma was always hurting Amie's... (8)
14 Amie has a band of laziness (6)
15 What part of Dandy's body got punched (4)
16 What sort of silver cow is Lottie (8)

DOWN

2 Crawling around like what sort of animal (6)
3 Irma, Amie, and Dandy—a love what (8)
4 They did not require her mind in turmoil (4)
5 She lied about knowing this actor (3, 7)
6 Slacker's namesake (3, 7)
9 What Dandy sang that Irma hated (8)
11 Lottie had an innate capacity for trouble (6)
13 This precious water bloom was ruined (4)

53

When Thieves Fall Out

The body of Dinah Mite has been found strangled in a shack in the village of Shady Corner. Superintendent U. Sless is having to wash his shoes after standing in a cow patty, so it is up to you to solve the crime.

NICK ASSETS

"I'll kill the person who did this!" snarled Nick. "I loved her!" Can he tell us who he thinks did it then? "That darned Southerner, Al. He's an explosives expert and was trying to buy some gelignite from us. He was going to blow up the festival being held at the Oriental Teahouse next week. Dinah was holding out—she'd upped the ante because of the risks involved. Our landlord is about to evict us now we've no salary coming in to pay rent on this dump. She was a pearl, and he's killed her!"

AL CATRAZ

"Well, now," drawled Al. "I didn't kill the little lady. She's got a body like Demi Moore and a face to match! And doesn't she remind me of Belle Starr, that gutsy American outlaw and rustler." In that case does he have any ideas? "Yessir, their cohort, Rob. I believe he has an itch to branch out on his own. Dinah caught him tampering with some oxygen cylinders they have out back, and had begun to speculate he was up to no good. I'd surely give three cheers to see him locked up!"

ROB BARRONS

"He's trying to frame me!" yelled Rob. "I didn't kill her!" Did he know who did? "Yes, it was Nick. He had cause to think she was less than happy with him. He thought we were getting together, but it was very much a case of 'never the twain'—she liked Al. Nick was suffering from acute jealousy. Why don't you go and grill him again, he's the one that did it!"

ACROSS

1 What Al wanted to blow up (8)
7 According to Nick, Dinah was precious (5)
8 He had reason to think she wasn't happy with him (5)
9 Al would give three hurrahs (6)
10 Dinah had a face and body to match this film star (4)
12 She was not so happy with him (4)
14 Rob was tampering with these cylinders (6)
17 Rob and Dinah—a case of never the two (5)
18 The landlord was about to oust them (5)
19 The teahouse to be blown up (8)

DOWN

1 Al was trying to trap Rob (5)
2 They had no wages to pay the rent (6)
3 Al thinks Rob had an urge to branch out (4)
4 The severe jealousy Nick was suffering from (5)
5 Dinah had begun to guess that Rob was up to no good (9)
6 Al was trying to buy explosives . . . (9)
11 . . . as he was an aficionado (6)
13 The surname of the American outlaw (5)
15 Rob wants you to interrogate Nick again (5)
16 Dinah had upped the stake (4)

A Hole in One

The body of Manny Quinn, the golf professional, has been found behind the clubhouse at Nether Bottom Golf Club. Superintendent U. Sless is still trying to sink his putt on the first hole so it is up to you to apprehend the murderer.

BEA LOWPAR

"How terrible, poor Manny," wailed Bea. "He was the kingpin of this club. So handsome, I always thought he looked like a younger Al Gore! And he had the wisdom of Solomon." Any idea who killed him? "That Lily, she's been trying to get extra coaching from Manny, but he just ignored her. She's been very anti since. She thinks he's been trying to foil her chances in the Ladies Cup, but he told me he doesn't like to get too close to her because her oral hygiene isn't very good—she overheard and was enraged!"

LILY PUTT

"Ridiculous!" snorted Lily. "Bea goes into a sulk if he so much as looks at another woman. Erik, the club janitor, saw him giving an expensive orchid to another woman and Bea shoved him in a bunker—spoilt his swing for a while, he could barely hobble." So who did it then? "Sandy—she was the other woman and had laid on a delicious spread—Lima Bean Casserole topped the menu, but he went crawling back to Bea."

SANDY TRAPP

"What rubbish!" laughed Sandy. "I was only trying to thank him for his extra coaching—my game has improved at a good rate." Any idea who it was then? "I think it was Bea—Manny is moving to Hawaii in a couple of months to be a golf pro on Maui, he's packing up lock, stock, and barrel. Manny's been trying to set up a domino run to raise funds—Bea in her fury trampled the lot and they had a terrible fight. She wanted to stop him leaving, and she's succeeded!"

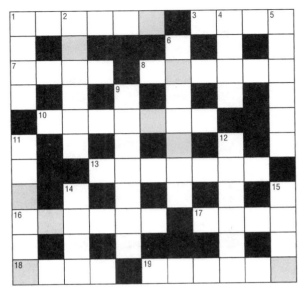

54

ACROSS

1 Bea ruined Manny's swing (6)
3 Lily thought he was trying to ruin her chances (4)
7 Manny was packing up —, stock, and barrel (4)
8 Where he was moving to (6)
10 Bea thought Manny was top dog of the club (7)
13 He had the wisdom of a biblical character (7)
16 Bea shoved Manny into a hole (6)
17 The bean used in a casserole (4)
18 Who saw Manny giving an expensive bloom (4)
19 Manny had the good looks of a younger who (2, 4)

DOWN

1 Bea goes into a mood if Manny looks at another woman (4)
2 The bloom given (6)
4 What hygiene was poor (4)
5 Sandy had put out a delicious spread (4, 2)
6 The job of **18A** (7)
9 Manny just snubbed Lily (7)
11 He could barely shuffle after he was shoved (6)
12 The type of run Manny was trying to set up (6)
14 Lily has been against Manny since she couldn't get the extra coaching (4)
15 Sandy's game has improved at a good pace (4)

Treacherous Waters

The horribly lacerated body of Phil O'Rupp has been found behind his boathouse at Shingle Bay. As Superintendent U. Sless has fallen in a lobster pot, it is once again up to you to catch the culprit.

TY DUP

"He was a born trouble-maker!" exclaimed Ty. "I think lots of people would have wanted him out of the way." Like who for example. "Lucy, for one, he embarrassed her terribly. They were invited to Oldham Grange by Olaf and Enid Spinks to attend a glittering party with a galaxy of personages parading around in their Armani outfits. Phil had far too much to drink and tried to caress his hostess in the shrubbery. Olaf kicked them both out!"

LUCY MARBLES

"Nonsense!" snorted Lucy. "What nerve!" Who was it then? "Ford, I suspect. Phil invited him out on his little boat, *The Orca*. Ford brought along his pen pal Gloria, who was visiting him before returning to Iran, where her husband works. There was something wrong with the engine and the fumes threatened to give them all asphyxia—they managed to get back alright but collapsed when they got ashore. Ford accused Phil of being a hired assassin and belted him!"

FORD RIVERS

"No way!" stated Ford. "You can't pin it on me!" Who did do it them? "I think it was Ty. Phil met a really genial fellow who told him about a thriller, based on true facts, that he was writing, about bandits in Sardinia. Phil was agog with excitement and began blabbing all the details around the county at a furious pace, without realizing it was Ty's clan he was talking about. Ty is the only one who would dare to take the law into his own hands—and he did!"

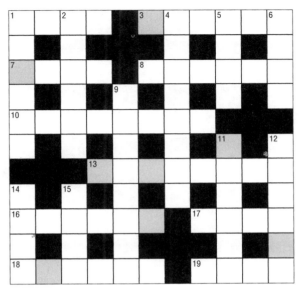

55

ACROSS

1 The boat's name (4)

3 They all collapsed when they got back on land (6)

7 Ty was the only one who would be brave enough to take the law into his own hands (4)

8 The designer clothing worn at the party (6)

10 Ford accused Phil of being a hired murderer (8)

13 The fellow was writing this type of novel (8)

16 A cosmos of personages (6)

17 Where the pen pal was from (4)

18 This fellow was writing the book (6)

19 Phil was blabbing at a furious speed (4)

DOWN

1 & **12D** Where the party was (6)

2 Phil tried to stroke his hostess (6)

4 Where the bandits are based (8)

5 The name of the host…(4)

6 …and the name of his wife (4)

9 They all nearly died from choking on the boat (8)

11 The name of the pen pal (6)

12 See **1D** (6)

14 Phil was eager with excitement (4)

15 It was Ty's tribe the fellow was talking about (4)

Cat-astrophe

The body of Pearl O'Wisdom has been found murdered in the Cattattackya Valley Cattery which she owned. As Superintendent U. Sless is allergic to cats, it is up to you to find the culprit.

LOU NATTICK

"Fancy Pearl being bumped off," exclaimed Lou. "There's been unrest here, but I didn't think morale had sunk that low!" Who did he think had killed Pearl? "That Honor—she's a weird one. What an outburst the other day! She had tied up Athena, Pearl's prize Persian—apparently caught her stalking a tawny owl chick. Pearl was furious!"

HONOR WHIM

"I didn't do it!" cried Honor. "Lou had better not start casting aspersions like that!" Did she have any ideas? "Yes! I think it was Jack—Pearl was going to have him thrown out because the cats give him hay fever and he wouldn't go down Broadway—the main alley between the cages. For the sake of the cats you can't have someone who won't go near them!"

JACK LADD

"What a load of twaddle," snorted Jack. "I wouldn't let hay fever stop me—I love cats! Athena especially, who would arch her back with pleasure and purr delightedly when I stroked her." Did he have any clues as to who did kill Pearl then? "Lou did! He escorted Pearl to the Hunt Ball last week. She's been in an abstract mood since, and very reticent about the dance. Just mutters about Lou and the chandelier! Something happened, and she hasn't even looked at him or spoken to him since!"

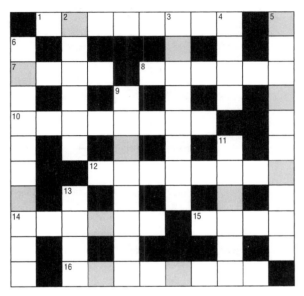

ACROSS

1 What a flare-up there was the other day (8)

7 The cat did this delightedly (4)

8 The name of the prized Persian (6)

10 Pearl was in a speculative mood (8)

12 The chick being stalked (5, 3)

14 Pearl was going to have Jack hurled out (6)

15 Honor's concern was the benefit of the cats (4)

16 The cats gave Jack this (3, 5)

DOWN

2 There was a bad feeling in the cattery (6)

3 Pearl was very diffident about the dance (8)

4 Honor had tethered the cat (4)

5 Pearl mutters about Lou and a ceiling ornament (10)

6 She evidently caught the cat stalking (10)

9 The alley between the cages (8)

11 Lou didn't realize this had sunk so low (6)

13 The cat would curve her back (4)

Commune-ity Killing

The body of Lou Screws has been found with a fatal head wound at the Happy Valley Commune. As Superintendent U. Sless has become entangled in his kaftan, it is up to you to catch the crook.

PHIL SCILLY

"I'm not surprised someone wanted him dead!" exclaimed Phil. "He was a weirdo. He hails from Ripon, but has travelled around chasing various esoteric fantasies. He drove a rickshaw in India for a year then was mugged, so left, without a rupee to his name. He came home and started attending Synagogue but was kicked out for playing *Apache*, by The Shadows, during services." Any idea who killed him? "Gladys—she is a svelte creature and he was always chasing after her. He put boot polish around the eyepiece of her binoculars, and thought it was funny. She didn't!"

GLADYS BACK

"I didn't do it!" said Gladys indignantly. "Although Phil's right—he was a nutter. He headed off to Corfu once. Felt he was the reincarnation of Apollo. More like King Canute—he sat on the beach saying he would halt the incoming tide. Unfortunately it was a spring tide—he should have waited until neap tides." Any clue as to who killed him? "Yes, it must have been Noah. His girlfriend is a nurse at the local hospital and Lou was forever there with an array of ailments, trying to seduce her. Noah wasn't happy about that!"

NOAH IDEA

"It wasn't me!" stated Noah. "Although we've all felt like it at one time or another. He claimed he was the president of a large commune on the Isle of Elba. We all took out membership and were going to move there, then he claimed our fees had been stolen by bandits. He then said the commune was going to annul our membership, and that was that—we lost a lot of money!" Who did he think had killed him then? "It was Phil—he was angry at the way Lou would sift through our belongings when we weren't around and said he was going to stop it for once and all!"

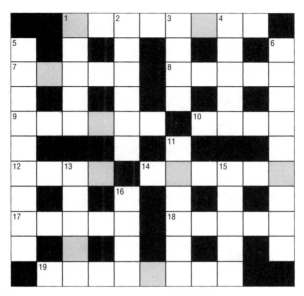

ACROSS

1 What Lou drove in India (8)
7 Where Lou hailed from (5)
8 He thought what he did to Gladys' binoculars was this (5)
9 She was a slim creature (6)
10 A commune was on this isle (4)
12 Phil wasn't surprised someone wanted Lou... (4)
14 Lou thought he was which Greek God (6)
17 Noah's girlfriend's job (5)
18 The Greek island Lou headed off to once (5)
19 The part of the binoculars that had boot polish applied (8)

DOWN

1 Lou didn't have a coin to his name when he left India (5)
2 The king he tried to emulate (6)
3 Lou would rifle through everyone's belongings (4)
4 The island commune was going to end their membership (5)
5 Lou claimed he was the leader of the commune (9)
6 He was kicked out of the temple (9)
11 The Shadows' tune (6)
13 Lou was always at the hospital with a range of ailments (5)
15 The commune was a big one (5)
16 Lou should have waited for this tide (4)

Musical Drama

The body of Sherry Drinker has been found murdered with brutal puncture wounds at the home of her ex-boyfriend. Superintendent U. Sless can't find a parking space for his car so it is up to you to find the culprit.

MACK MUSIC

"I'm sorry Sherry has been killed," said Mack, "but she was a horrid pest." Did he know who did it? "Possibly Noel, another ex-boyfriend—he was entertaining his friends Alec and Dora Reid. They'd just returned from touring Iberia and were heading home to the Mendips. They brought a friend to introduce to him—Emmy—and they were very taken with each other. Sherry burst in, tipsy as usual—not a pretty aspect—and began to vent her spleen about how he had used her and then dumped her. He was furious."

NOEL TONE

"Rubbish!" snapped Noel. "I didn't kill her." Any ideas who did? "I think it was Belle—she's an item with Mack now and Sherry was out to get her. When they had a musical soiree, Sherry burst in drunk and had almost cajoled Mack to return to her. Belle waded in almost as a reflex action, going for her tooth and claw. Sherry backed off and spat abuse from afar. They certainly had it in for each other!"

BELLE CANTOR

"Nonsense!" stated Belle. "He's the editor of some pretty malicious gossip, isn't he!" If it wasn't her who was it then? "I'm very afraid it was Mack—he loves his music, likes to compose his own pieces and adores Vivaldi. He likes the *Blue Danube* as well, one of my favorites, but whenever Mack was having a musical evening, Sherry would butt in and put on *Yeoman of the Guard* or whatever, which made him cringe. He's a star in a lot of ways but she always managed to infuriate him—she went too far this time!"

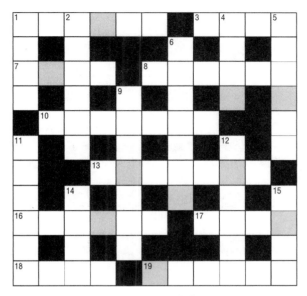

_58_

ACROSS

1 Sherry's choice of music made Mack flinch (6)

3 See **7A** (4)

7 The name of Noel's male friend (4)

8 Sherry's taste in music, — *of the Guard* (6)

10 Mack adores this composer (7)

13 He likes to make up his own pieces (7)

16 Belle waded in with almost an instinctive action (6)

17 Sherry gave release to her spleen (4)

18 Noel's friend's wife (4)

19 Noel was the originator of some malicious gossip (6)

DOWN

1 Belle went for Sherry with tooth and... (4)

2 From where had the friends just returned (6)

4 The friend of the friends (4)

5 The *Blue* river tune is one of Belle's favorites (6)

6 Where the friends were heading home to (7)

9 Sherry had almost coaxed Mack to return to her (7)

11 Sherry was a nasty pest (6)

12 Sherry, tipsy as usual, was not a pretty vision (6)

14 Sherry spat abuse from a long way off (4)

15 Mack's a VIP in a lot of ways (4)

Flash Point!

The hideously strangled body of Ethel Een has been found behind a tree at Lesser Slaughter Village. As Superintendent U. Sless is busy raking up leaves, it is once again your job to carry out the investigation and catch the culprit.

AL OVER

"An extremely odd woman!" exclaimed Al. "Rather a close alliance with the bottle, I believe." Who did he think had killed her? "It was probably Jack Flash. He had just finished preparing his arable land for sowing when the damsel in question stole a motorbike from his garage and began to harass him, throwing all sorts of missiles and tearing up his newly ploughed field. That totally enraged him!"

JACK FLASH

"It most certainly wasn't me!" stated Jack, "although I claim a near miss for the way I was feeling!" In that case, who was it? "Ava is very likely. She was at the end of her tether. She was holding a fete in her garden to start a fund for the church roof. Ethel turned up rather the worse for wear, clad in a gold lamé dress, with her father's old military kepi perched on the top of her head! She fell into the pool, but being unable to swim, Ava had to leap in and rescue her. All in front of the priest!"

AVA TOFFEE

"I most emphatically did not do it!" declared Ava. "What nerve!" Who did it then? "Al is the guilty one. He was lying in his hammock, reading a book about East Anglia written by his brother Adam. Ethel was trying to aspire to even greater heights of stupidity by driving her car whilst under the influence. She got her jacket sleeve caught in the gear lever and lost control and drove straight into him. Took hours to unwind them both. He was furious!"

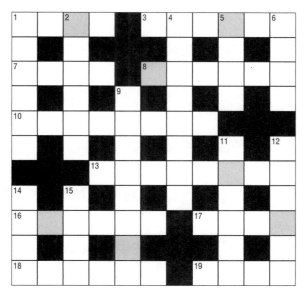

ACROSS

1 The lever Ethel got caught up in (4)

3 Her activities served to totally madden Jack (6)

7 Al was trying to peruse a book (4)

8 Ethel began to do pester Jack (6)

10 The dress she wore (4, 4)

13 What did she keep throwing at Jack (8)

16 It took hours to unravel Al and Ethel (6)

17 Ethel's headwear (4)

18 The woman in question stole a motorbike (6)

19 The gala Ava was holding in her garden (4)

DOWN

1 Where the motorbike was stolen from (6)

2 Jack was preparing land for crops (6)

4 Jack can claim a close shave (4, 4)

5 The name of Al's brother (4)

6 The part of Anglia the book was about (4)

9 Ethel had a link with the bottle (8)

11 The arm of her jacket got caught in the lever (6)

12 Ethel was trying to reach even greater heights of stupidity (6)

14 The gala was to start a collection (4)

15 Ethel couldn't do this so Ava had to rescue her (4)

Aced!

The body of Art Strings has been found murdered at the Green Lawns Tennis Club.
As Superintendent U. Sless has become entangled in the net, it is up to you,
his trusty assistant, to catch the culprit.

WALTER DRIP

"Art wasn't very popular," sniffed Walter. "He thought he was top dog at the club, and was beginning to alienate everybody!" Did he have any clues as to who might have killed him? "I think it was probably Dolly—she was in love with him right from the outset but he wasn't interested, already had a woman friend. She always caused quite a stir, wafting clouds of aromatic perfume towards the courts, sitting in the royal box—as we call our celebrity seats! If you ask me, he was nothing more than a gigolo!"

DOLLY VOLLEY

"What a load of claptrap" snorted Dolly. "I liked Art, but that was all. No strategy when we played doubles, and inclined to skew all over the court, but not a bad fellow!" Any ideas who might have killed him? "Oh, dear, I don't really like to point the finger, but I think Lorna could have! Art had a terrible fight with her big brother, and put Eddy in hospital, and I don't think she's ever forgiven him for that!"

LORNA TANNIS

"What nonsense," Lorna cried. "It's all a pose with her—acting as our resident pacifist. She has no idea what is really going on!" In that case, did she know what had happened? "Yes, I do! You don't need a degree in psychology to know that Walter was jealous of Art. A drip by name and a drip by nature. He would never give any leeway on the courts to Art, nor off. He hated him, and wanted him out of the way!"

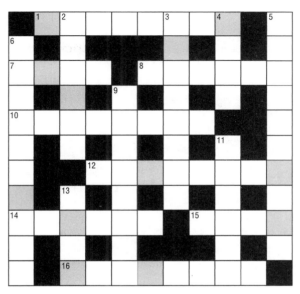

ACROSS

1 Art was beginning to estrange everybody... (8)

7 ...and inclined to do this all over the court... (4)

8 He thought he was a big cheese at the club (3, 3)

10 Dolly thought it was a load of this (8)

12 She was the resident peace-lover (8)

14 Dolly was in love with him right from the start (6)

15 It's all a pretence with Dolly (4)

16 The celebrity seats (5, 3)

DOWN

2 Walter never gave any slack to Art (6)

3 Clouds of sweet-smelling perfume (8)

4 The name of Lorna's sibling (4)

5 His relationship to her (3, 7)

6 You don't need a degree in this subject (10)

9 Art didn't have tactics when he played doubles (8)

11 If you asked Walter, he would say Art was nothing more than a playboy (6)

13 The girlfriend always caused a commotion (4)

Fortune's Fate

The body of Ivor Fortune has been found brutally murdered at his country home, Nouveau Gables. As Superintendent U. Sless is being held hostage in his car by six large Rottweilers, it is up to you to find the culprit.

MILLIE O'NAIR

"How horrible," cried Millie. "We were getting married in two weeks!" Did she know who killed him? "Yes, his good-for-nothing son, Connor! He is a morose individual. He sits around all day playing his sitar and he goes to the mosque to worship—his father was heartbroken to have raised such a bum! He found him rummaging through the bureau in the library and when he challenged him, Connor threatened his father with a knife! It made me quake with terror!"

CONNOR FORTUNE

"Absolute rubbish!" snorted Connor. "I didn't do the old boy in." Did he know who did? "I reckon it was Rosie. But I think she didn't mean to kill him, I think she was after Millie—she was jealous of her in her cashmere sweaters, sipping her fine Loire wines and holidays in Ibiza, and boasting about her family's stained-glass window in the apse at the church. Rosie wanted to marry a rich man and she's not one to skirt a problem—she tackles it head on!"

ROSIE FLOTSAM

"What a mesh of lies!" exclaimed Rosie with heat. "I have money of my own—I won the lotto twice in Australia last year!" In that case, did she know who had done the dirty deed? "It was Millie—she likes to come across as a lady, and orate pompously on every subject under the sun! But underneath her facade of gentility she was akin to a virago. When Ivor wanted to go and watch the All Blacks play, she was so enraged, she stuttered and spluttered and couldn't produce a coherent syllable! Then she chased the poor man around the garden brandishing a loofah at him! It was actually quite hilarious!"

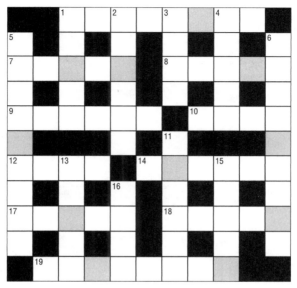

ACROSS

1 Millie couldn't produce a coherent sound (8)
7 How Rosie won the money (5)
8 She's not one to go around a problem (5)
9 What Connor was rummaging through (6)
10 Rosie exclaimed with fervor (4)
12 Millie was like a virago (4)
14 Connor was a sulky individual (6)
17 Connor threatened his father with a weapon (5)
18 It made Millie tremble with terror (5)
19 The wool her sweaters were made from (8)

DOWN

1 Connor's instrument (5)
2 Millie was brandishing this at Ivor (6)
3 In which part of the church was the stained glass window (4)
4 Origin of the wines (5)
5 Ivor wanted to watch this team play (3, 6)
6 Millie was so enraged she spluttered and stammered (9)
11 Connor's place of worship (6)
13 The holiday isle (5)
15 Millie liked to speak pompously (5)
16 What a net of lies, according to Rosie (4)

Dramatic Endings

The body of Adam Pest has been found poisoned in the townhall at Much Muckle. Superintendent U.Sless has been held up by a herd of cows, so it is up to you to solve the crime.

VERA PRETTY

"What a shock," exclaimed Vera. "Imagine Adam being killed—still managing to cause a hubbub, even in death." Any idea who could have done it? "Oh, yes, I think it was Russell. He's our leading light in the amateur dramatics and Adam had recently joined the cast. His ridiculous antics roused Russell into terrible rages. I mean, Adam rode his bike onto the stage, wearing Bermuda shorts in the most outrageous day-glo yellow color just as Russell was delivering Hamlet's famous soliloquy—I thought he'd have a heart attack!"

RUSSELL PAPER

"Nonsense!" snapped Russell. "What gall to accuse me." Any clues then as to who did do it? "Wouldn't put it past Ina—Adam was always winding her up. He drilled a small eyelet in the wall between the dressing rooms and used it to spy on her. Made her furious. Then he put an old piece of stilton cheese under the floorboards—the smell was dreadful! Took her ages to fathom the cause. The more she raged the more it seemed to spur him on."

INA FIX

"What a lot of rot!" stormed Ina. "I certainly didn't do it." Who did then? "Miss La-di-dah Vera would be my guess. Tries to appear sophisticated but really is quite gauche. She was showing off her smart friends, Abel and Honora Mandela from Iowa—you could almost hear Adam mull over how best to get maximum reaction. Vera sat her guests in our dress circle to watch rehearsal. Adam locked the door and then let off a smoke bomb. The ensuing panic was dreadful—Vera just let out a massive squall! Give that man an inch and he'd take a mile!"

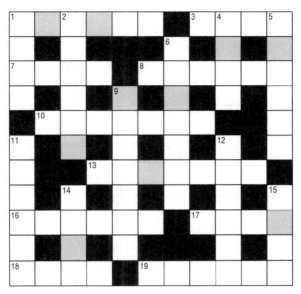

ACROSS

1 The friends were sat in the dress — to watch rehearsal (6)

3 What did Adam ride on to the stage (4)

7 The more Ina raged the more it seemed to egg Adam on (4)

8 Vera was really quite awkward (6)

10 Adam's shorts (7)

13 The cheese under the floorboards (7)

16 Adam was still causing a furor even in death (6)

17 The American state (4)

18 You could almost hear Adam ponder (4)

19 Vera let out a massive cry (6)

DOWN

1 Adam had recently joined the crew (4)

2 His silly antics always prompted Russell to anger (6)

4 Give Adam a tiny measurement and he'd take a mile (4)

5 What was drilled in the wall (6)

6 The surname of the Americans (7)

9 The type of dramatics (7)

11 It took ages for Ina to work out a cause (6)

12 The first name of the Iowan woman (6)

14 The Iowan man's first name (4)

15 What impudence to accuse Russell (4)

63

Mucky Murder

The body of Carl Farmer had been found, with dreadful lacerations, behind the manure pile on his farm. As Superintendent U. Sless is admiring the baby lambs, it is up to you to apprehend the culprit.

NOEL GOODE

"What a horrible thing to happen!" cried Noel. "I was very fond of him." Any idea who did it? "I wouldn't put it past that Bea. I think she is a bit cuckoo—hasn't got a job and lives on her welfare checks each week. I'm pretty sure she was trying to chisel money out of him. I also know that he bought her a gold bracelet—I'm surprised she hasn't sold it yet. All that girl does is sit and watch her favorite videos all day—*The Bridge on The River Kwai* and *Get Carter*. Get farmer, more likely!"

BEA LYNE

"It wasn't me!" exclaimed Bea. "But sure, I asked him for money; he's got plenty. Always took an annual trip; Iraq last year, Sri Lanka this. It's not fair!" Did she know who did do it? "His farm manager, Bernie, is the culprit. He's a serious wino and has been known to imbibe far too much. The other night he got drowsy and dozed off. He didn't hear when the barn burst into flames and the new colt was squealing and the oxen bellowing. It was ablaze for hours. Carl was furious!"

BERNIE PAPERS

"Not true!" snorted Bernie. "It's a pack of lies!" So, who did do it then? "That useless step-brother of his—Noel. He was playing with matches and started the fire. Carl was fearless in his attempts to put out the blaze. Laid into Noel afterwards with an umbrella. We had to band together to stop him. He was acid in his condemnation of that twit—asked him what he did for an encore. Now we know—murder!"

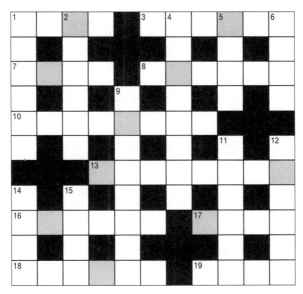

ACROSS

1 Where Carl went last year (4)
3 Noel thinks Bea is a bit this (6)
7 They had to get together to stop Carl (4)
8 The barn was flaming for hours (6)
10 Carl bought Bea a gold one (8)
13 Where Carl went this year (3, 5)
16 Noel was sure Bea was trying to extract money out of Carl (6)
17 The new pony was squealing (4)
18 Bernie got tired and dozed off (6)
19 And he didn't listen to the fire start (4)

DOWN

1 Bernie had been known to drink a bit too much (6)
2 Carl always took a yearly trip (6)
4 Carl laid into Noel with this (8)
5 The bridge was on what river (4)
6 What were bellowing (4)
9 Carl was unafraid in his attempts to put out the fire (8)
11 He asked Noel what he did for a bravo (6)
12 *Get* — was another favorite video (6)
14 Carl was biting in his condemnation (4)
15 Bernie was a serious drinker (4)

Battered Beauty

The body of Leo Nyne, manager of Nutley Village's beauty salon, Beauty Within and Without, has been found brutally murdered. Superintendent U. Sless has stopped to feed the ducks on the village green, so it is once again up to you to solve the heinous crime.

MINNIE CURIST

"Oooh, isn't it awful!" Minnie trilled. "Our boss being killed like that. Mind you, he was a bit of an ogre with a temper to match. Talk about a rugged he-man. We called him Eric the Red, because of his red hair." Any ideas who might have killed him then? "Well, it could be Holly. He made her cry yesterday, and she looked a sight with her eyeliner smudged. She's been to Reno, in Nevada, and had a facelift there and he told her that whatever she paid for it, it wasn't worth it!"

HOLLY DAY

"And I thought she was my friend!" exclaimed Holly. "Seems like I've nurtured a serpent in my bosom!" Did she have a clue to the identity of the killer? "Probably that Clair—she hated him. She asked for a raise because her rent has gone up and he told her she was a useless ornament who wasn't worth what she was paid, let alone deserving of a raise! If it comes to a crunch, I reckon she did it!"

CLAIR SKY

"She's talking like an inhabitant of outer space!" said Clair. "She hasn't got a clue!" Did she? "Oh, yes, it's a clear-cut case—Minnie did it! She is nutty about animals and he had threatened to bisect the stray cat she's been feeding. His estimate was that it was costing us five dollars a week. She was furious and threw that fern over yonder at him and cut his forehead. He was going to fire her!"

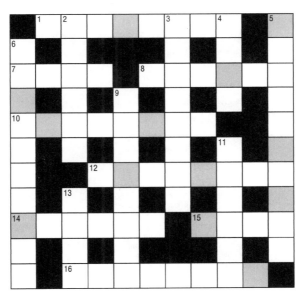

ACROSS

1 What was smudged (8)
7 Where Holly had been in Nevada (4)
8 If it came to this, Clair did it (6)
10 What sort of case is it (5-3)
12 What surgery was done in the States (8)
14 Leo was a strapping he-man (6)
15 The plant over **2D** that was thrown (4)
16 Leo's guess (8)

DOWN

2 See **15A** (6)
3 How the serpent in the bosom was treated (8)
4 Clair's lease has gone up... (4)
5 ...and she thinks Holly is talking like a native from outer space (10)
6 Leo's nickname (4, 3, 3)
9 One of the girls was called a useless knick-knack (8)
11 Leo was going to do this to the stray cat (6)
13 He was a bit of a monster (4)

Billy Butts Out

The poisoned body of Bill Egote has been found in the barn at Runnybrook Farm. Superintendent U. Sless has unfortunately driven his car into the cesspool so it is up to you to solve the crime.

NAN EGOTE

"What a calamity!" exclaimed Nan. "It will be hard to run this place without my brother." Does she have any idea who killed him? "I think it was Roland. He is the quintessential Peter Pan. He sat in the kitchen last night, listening to a tenor on the radio, conducting the music, waving his arms around like that André Previn! He's Orcadian, but found it hard to make a living there, so moved here last year. He hasn't an ounce of sense, and his stupidity has cost us money in ruined crops. He will argue all the time, and doesn't ever learn from his mistakes. Bill was going to fire him."

ROLAND BUTTER

"I didn't do it!" cried Roland. "I was eager to leave here and return home anyway!" Any clue to the killer then? "Yes, Henry, he's a funny one! He put poison in the squirrel's nest and kept chuckling about Dr. Crippen. Then he gave an olive to the collie and it nearly choked. Everyone is scared of him, wondering when he's going to start trying to kill people—he probably poisoned the diet shrimp paste Bill has on his sandwiches!"

HENRY ETTALAM

"What a load of inane rubbish!" snorted Henry. "Bill asked me to get rid of the squirrels. It certainly wasn't me." Who was it then. "It was that sister of his, Nan. She swans around here in an aura of Dior perfume. She was trying to urge him to sell up. She wanted the money, then she would be able to marry her boyfriend, Philip. She is normally able to twirl Bill around her little finger, but not this time, so she poisoned him!"

ACROSS

1 Roland's nationality (8)
7 Nan could normally twist Bill around her little finger (5)
8 Roland was keen to leave (5)
9 The conductor he copied (6)
10 Roland moved there last what (4)
12 Nan swans around in an aura of this perfume (4)
14 Her boyfriend's name (6)
17 The singer Roland was listening to on the radio (5)
18 A load of trite rubbish (5)
19 Roland is this quintessentially (5, 3)

DOWN

1 What the dog ate (5)
2 What sort of dog was it (6)
3 Bill's lightweight shrimp paste (4)
4 Roland would row all the time (5)
5 His folly cost them money (9)
6 Henry chuckled about this person (2, 7)
11 The sort of paste Bill had on his sandwiches (6)
13 Roland hasn't got a bit of sense (5)
15 He doesn't ever improve from his mistakes (5)
16 Nan was trying to incite Bill to sell (4)

Medieval Mystery

The body of Connor Punter has been found brutally murdered in the hall of his medieval house in the village of Nether Bottom. Superintendent U. Sless has fallen into the moat so it is up to you to catch the culprit.

MILLIE PEDE

"Oh, what a terrible shock!" cried Millie. "A regular pal he was. You should have seen him when he was dressed up in top hat and tails. Such a warm friendly manner, he would always call out to me on my arrival each morning to start the cleaning." Any idea who killed him? "His nephew, Roger, is a trouble-maker. He's not got an iota of affection in his body. He got into trouble in Europe, driving that fancy Sierra of his and fell foul of the various border patrols for his hectic speeds. Mr. Punter was going to disinherit him!"

ROGER DODGER

"What drivel that woman talks," sneered Roger. "My uncle wasn't the great friend she thought. His reputation was mud in the private sector of business. He made most of his money through shady deals. My Aunt Titania left him because of his ways!" Any clues to the killer? "His secretary, Hal, was a bit of a bad egg as well. Uncle had reason to believe he stole a black opal of great rarity. He had a file an inch thick on him. I think Hal killed him to escape justice."

HAL TAKIT

"Nonsense!" exclaimed Hal. "Connor and I had an excellent relationship. It is not I who is suspected of taking the gem—it is him! He is thought to have swallowed it! I wanted an X-ray taken but Connor wouldn't hear of it!" Did he know who killed him then? "Millie has been slowly robbing Connor blind. She's hiding valuables under her tabard and in her voluminous shopping bag. He used some sort of indelible green marker, and she ended up with dyed fingers! He confronted her with the fact after a beautiful silver bowl, used for mixing the stirrup cup for the local hunt, was stolen. He was going to call the police and she prevented him, permanently!"

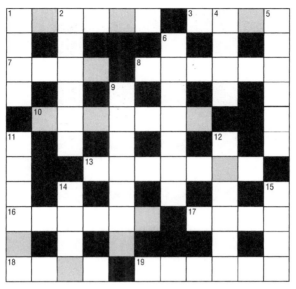

66

ACROSS

1 The nephew fell foul of these patrols (6)

3 This dossier was an inch thick (4)

7 Connor had an affable friendly manner (4)

8 His reputation was mud in the private area of business (6)

10 The cup mixed for the hunt (7)

13 The aunt's name (7)

16 Dressed up in this headwear and tails (3, 3)

17 Hal wanted a picture taken (1-3)

18 Connor would always shout to Millie in the morning when she got there (4)

19 Millie was hiding valuables under what (6)

DOWN

1 A silver what was stolen (4)

2 A gem of great uniqueness went missing (6)

4 Roger didn't have this amount of affection in his body (4)

5 He got into bother on the continent (6)

6 Connor was a real gent (7)

9 He always greeted Millie on her entrance in the morning (7)

11 Roger's speeds (6)

12 What sort of car did he drive (6)

14 The gem stolen (4)

15 Millie ended up with colored fingers (4)

The Madding Crowd

The horrifically murdered body of Dr. Goode has been found in his office at the Happy Valley Asylum. As Superintendent U. Sless is too scared to enter the building in case they commit him, it is up to you to conclude the investigation.

ALI BARBAR

"Oh, fancy our big chief being done in!" exclaimed Ali. Did he know who had done it? "It was Wally. The aliens were after him but he couldn't get Interpol to help him. He stuck to the Doc like a limpet thinking he'd be protected, but he heard him talking fluent Arabic to me and thought he'd been taken over by the extraterrestrials! That's why he killed him!"

WALLY NUTTE

"Not me, not me!" cried Wally. Who was it then? "It was Mike—there's a maniac if ever there was one. He thought he was a mole, and kept trying to burrow into the velvet curtains. Then he turned vegetarian. He stopped eating cheese when he heard the curdling agent—rennet—was an animal product and would only eat leek soup. Any mention of a meat cutlet would test his temper sorely. He then tried to get the Doc to impose a levy on anyone who touched meat. Doc refused and Mike killed the poor gent!"

MIKE MADDER

"It wasn't me!" shouted Mike. In that case, who was it? "It was Ali. He believed he was an Emir from the Middle East. And he claimed fame and fortune would be his because he rode the only unleaded camel in the world! He had a spear which he claimed was from the stone age and had been left to him by his uncle. He will ever and anon be a nutcase. The Doc was about to update the records and said Ali's eventual fate would be a straitjacket. So Ali thought he could forestall that and killed him!"

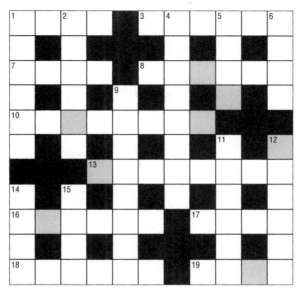

67

ACROSS

1 Mike wanted to impose this on meat-eaters (4)

3 Any mention of a joint of meat would upset his temper (6)

7 Mike thought he was this animal (4)

8 Wally thought Martians were after him (6)

10 Ali's ultimate fate would be a straitjacket (8)

13 Wally couldn't get this organization to help him (8)

16 Mike was a madman if ever there was one (6)

17 Ali claimed renown and fortune would be his (4)

18 What is the curdling agent (6)

19 Mike killed the poor man (4)

DOWN

1 Wally stuck to the Doc like an animal (6)

2 Mike tried to burrow into the curtain material (6)

4 Ali claimed his camel was what (8)

5 Mike would only eat this soup (4)

6 And mentioning meat would try his temper sorely (4)

9 What era was the spear from (5, 3)

11 The Doc was going to overhaul his records (6)

12 He spoke Arabic perfectly (6)

14 Ali thought he was a leader from the Middle East (4)

15 When will Ali be a nutcase (4)

Christmas Cracker

The body of May Haggle has been found murdered in the house of her son where she has been staying with her husband. Superintendent U. Sless is busy checking out the leftover turkey, so it is up to you to find out who the murderer is.

WOODY HAGGLE

"I am very upset about my mother," stated Woody, "but I must admit, she wasn't easy!" In that case, has he any idea who had killed her? "Much as I love my father, I think he did. She nagged him day and night and even went into overtime! He had to ask her permission if he wanted to go out alone. He felt less than adequate. Coming here, as they crossed the Pennines, he ran over a mute swan and she nagged the rest of the way. We've had segments of the incident on and off all Xmas. I think he flipped his lid and killed her!"

LES HAGGLE

"No, no! I didn't kill my wife!" exclaimed Les. "It is entirely untrue and idle speculation by my son!" Did he have any clue as to who did kill her? "Yes, I believe it was Glenda, my son's girlfriend. May has been very offensive about her cooking—the broccoli was overcooked and she called it green slime. Every now and then she'd put out a feeler as to how far she could go. She told Glenda she was too much of a reader and that's why she couldn't hold a decent conversation!

Poor Glenda, she was in a terrible state last night!"

GLENDA HAND

"I was in a terrible state, ergo I killed her—is that it?" queried Glenda. "No way!" Did she know who had? "It was Woody. May was exhaustive in her attempts to sabotage everything, he was fuming. Never invite your in-laws for Christmas! She's been trying to break up our relationship and get him to go back home to live! It was a flop last time he lived with her, no reason to suppose it would be different this time. He had just had enough!"

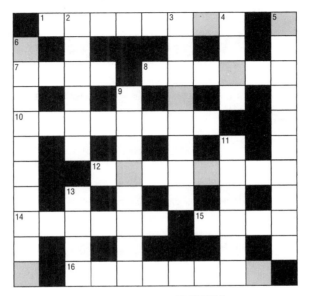

ACROSS

1 What vegetable was like green slime (8)

7 Yuletide (4)

8 May put this out now and then to test the air (6)

10 Les felt less than this (8)

12 They had these pieces on and off (8)

14 Don't invite these for Christmas (2-4)

15 Glenda was in a terrible state therefore she killed her (4)

16 Mountains Les and May crossed (8)

DOWN

2 Glenda was too much of a bookworm (6)

3 She went into this with her nagging (8)

4 See **11D** (4)

5 Les had to ask for consent to go out alone (10)

6 May was this in her sabotage attempts (10)

9 What was run over (4, 4)

11 & **4D** The speculation was false and pointless (4)

13 It was a disaster when Woody lived with his parents (4)

Weeded Out!

Down at Dingle Dell Cottage the body of Paul Bearer has been found poisoned in the herb garden. Superintendent U. Sless has fallen in a patch of stinging nettles so it is once again up to you to discover the killer.

DAISY CHAIN

"My goodness," exclaimed Daisy. "What a horrible thing to happen!" Did she know who had killed Paul? "Probably his girlfriend, April. They had a nasty fight yesterday. He was off to Ewood Park again. He always takes his nephews so they can sit in the family enclosure. He reckons it's a stampede on the terraces. April was incensed—he had promised to cut the bushes right down, they've been overrun by adders in the garden. She even found an adder in the bathroom!"

APRIL SHOWERS

"That woman is so obtuse," groaned April. "It wasn't me." Who was it then? "His so-called best friend, Lee. He's always around here, trying to scrounge money, drinks, cigars. He's so tight, he won't so much as buy a pint in the bar even though he drinks like a fish—he must be a Pisces. He was trying to sell Paul an old U.S. gold eagle he claims he was given, but Paul was very uneasy about it. He thought Lee was trying to dupe him with stolen goods!"

LEE MANNS

"What a pack of nonsense," said Lee. "The coin was an item left to me by my Uncle Andre who recently died. "In that case, did he know who had killed Paul? "That dreadful woman who lives next door—she presents a visage of erudition to the world, claims kinship with the explorer Amundsen, and is up on the works of Wilde. She likes to allot spare time to various charities as well. But Paul discovered she was into pagan pursuits and was going to expose her—Daisy has a terrible temper and pity the person who crosses her—as Paul did!"

ACROSS

1 The explorer Daisy claimed
   kinship with (8)
7 The writer she was up on (5)
8 The pursuits Daisy was into (5)
9 April thought Daisy was stupid (6)
10 Lee was trying to trade a gold
   coin (4)
12 Feel sorry for the person who
   crosses Daisy (4)
14 He was always trying to scrounge
   money, drinks, and what (6)
17 Paul had promised to cut the
   bushes down all the way (5)
18 April found a snake in the
   bathroom (5)
19 It's always a panic on the
   terraces (8)

DOWN

1 Daisy likes to apportion her spare
   time to various charities (5)
2 Paul felt uncomfortable about the
   purchase (6)
3 Paul thought Lee was trying to fool
   him (4)
4 The U.S. gold coin (5)
5 Paul was off to these grounds
   again (5, 4)
6 He took his nephews so he could
   sit in the family compound (9)
11 Daisy's face of erudition (6)
13 Lee was so mean (5)
15 Lee's uncle (5)
16 The coin was an object left by an
   uncle (4)

Secret Slaughter

The body of Carmen Secret has been found murdered in her cottage in Old Town. Superintendent U. Sless has been delayed with a flat tire so it is up to you to find the killer.

POPPY FIELD

"What a tragedy!" cried Poppy. "Such a popular lady, she used to bake a lot—her vanilla sponge cake was a real treat. Anybody was welcome to roll up at any time for a cup of tea and a chat. Such a blithe spirit." Any idea who killed her? "Her son Ivor is my bet. He usually stays in Exeter but has been home a while. He was such a cherub when a little boy but is definitely a bit odd now. He thinks there is a puma on the loose on Exmoor and spends his time hunting it. He's broke and wanted money but Carmen wouldn't give him any more!"

IVOR SECRET

"What a puny motive for murder!" exclaimed Ivor. "I loved my mother dearly and would never harm her. She and my father always did their best for me. I went to Eton for my education, thanks to them." Did he have any clues who killed her then? "There is a fellow hanging around, Ed, I think his name is. As I recall he has been courting my mother since he gleaned the fact she had money. She didn't flaunt it but he found out. He's a bit crafty, he helped her stencil the hallway! Apparently they had a row and he tried to strike her—she told him to get lost and he vowed to get even!"

ED HUNTER

"Nonsense!" said Ed. "I certainly did not kill her. Even though we had a falling out, amid all the trouble I was still very fond of her." Who did then? "Her so-called best friend Poppy. I may be no sage, but I could certainly detect the animosity between them. Poppy had drawn an outline of an extension she wanted built, and Carmen wrote a letter to the council with her objections. Poppy cursed her rotten and said she'd make sure she danced a reel or two on her grave. Looks like she's got her chance!"

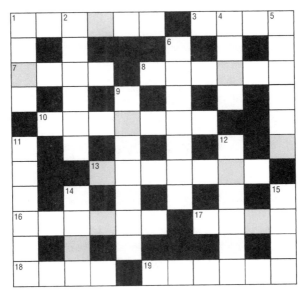

70

ACROSS

1 As Ivor did remember about Ed courting his mother (6)

3 Carmen used to cook a lot (4)

7 Ed vowed to get revenge (4)

8 And he tried to hit Carmen (6)

10 Poppy had drawn a sketch of an extension she wanted (7)

13 The flavor of the sponge that was a treat (7)

16 Carmen wrote a note to the council (6)

17 Ivor thinks this big cat is on the loose (4)

18 A weak motive for murder (4)

19 Carmen was this sort of spirit (6)

DOWN

1 Poppy was going to dance one or two on her grave (4)

2 Ivor was no angel when he was a little lad (6)

4 Ed was still fond of Carmen in the middle of the trouble (4)

5 Where Ivor is usually domiciled (6)

6 Ed helped Carmen paint her hallway (7)

9 Ed gathered that Carmen had money (7)

11 Anybody was welcome to arrive at any time (4, 2)

12 Carmen didn't show off about her money but Ed still found out (6)

14 Where Ivor got his education (4)

15 Ed might not be a wise man (4)

71

My Giddy Aunt!

The body of Winn Bagge had been found brutally strangled behind her cottage in Nether Bottom. As Superintendent U. Sless is being chased off by a flock of geese, it is up to you to catch the culprit.

CORA NAPPLE

"What a dreadful thing to happen to Aunt Winn!" exclaimed Cora. "Mind you, she was a frightful busybody at times, forever on the doorstep of her cronies." Any idea who killed her? "Carina was quite candid about her dislike of her. She is our local driving instructor, and Auntie was always raising Cain about the learners practising outside the cottage. Last time she complained, she sat on Carina's new settee and it split right across the base. Carina was furious and told her she must weigh more than a bull elephant!"

CARINA WASHE

"It most certainly was not me!" stated Carina. "Look elsewhere!" Where, in that case? "Our local cookery expert—Coco. She has a very casual approach to cooking but she's an expert in everything. She can cook brilliant Kosher food and delightful sponge cakes, and her Yule Log is out of this world! Winn, unfortunately, claimed the cakes always left a hard knot in her stomach, a solid mass causing indigestion. Coco has been heard to say she would gladly throttle the old so-and-so!"

COCO BUTTER

"I might have said it in the past!" agreed Coco. "But I didn't carry it out!" Who did in that case? "I think her niece Cora is the guilty one. She moved over from Ottawa with the intention of looking after her aunt in her old age. She wanted to pamper her, and shower her with acts of kindness. Unfortunately, Winn just carries on with a dour expression, offering not a word of thanks. Cora had likened her to a stuffed pike! Not only that, the silly old fool once poured chlorine bleach down the drain and the resulting fumes made them ill for ages. Cora was not best pleased!"

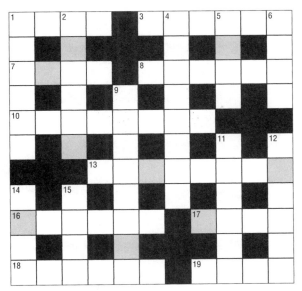

ACROSS

1 Winn resembled a stuffed fish (4)
3 Coco would happily throttle the old so-and-so (6)
7 The cakes were a solid weight causing indigestion (4)
8 Coco had a relaxed approach to her cooking (6)
10 Carina told Winn she must weigh more than this bull animal (8)
13 Winn was forever on her cronies' stoop (8)
16 Carina was quite blunt about her dislike of Winn (6)
17 Winn was always raising this (4)
18 She sat on Carina's new sofa (6)
19 She split it across the bottom (4)

DOWN

1 Cora wanted to look after her aunt (6)
2 Coco was brilliant at this sort of food (6)
4 Winn was always complaining about these practising outside the cottage (8)
5 She had this expression (4)
6 This log is out of this world (4)
9 The bleach poured down the drain (8)
11 Where the niece came from (6)
12 This type of cake is delightful (6)
14 Cora wanted to shower her aunt with deeds of kindness (4)
15 Winn claimed the cakes left a hard ball in her stomach (4)

Creative Killing

The body of inventor Mike Ansell has been found, brutally murdered, in his workshop in the little village of Chuckle Cross. Superintendent U. Sless has unfortunately gone to Cruckle Choss, so it is up to you to solve the crime.

CLAUDE HOPPER

"Not a very nice business, this," exclaimed Claude, "Mike was at the pinnacle of his creativeness and had recently enlarged his workforce." Did he have any idea who might have killed him? "Probably Ivor. Mike had some top secret inventions he was about to sell to the navy. Ivor is from Odessa, and I guess he was trying to steal them. He has been rather edgy lately!"

IVOR RECORD

"What a farcical notion!" snorted Ivor. "I am no Russian spy! Does Claude think he is Dr. Watson, helping Holmes to solve crimes?" Did he have any clues who could have done it? "I believe it was Sam, nasty piece of work. Seems to live in a cave in the sycamore forest, with a great black dog called Noah, and he stalks around in a pith helmet. He was always accusing Mike of living in capitalist opulence. They were always at each others' throats!"

SAM HOPE

"What a dope that Russkie is —a choice nugget!" laughed Sam. "Mike and I are friends that go way back. A little arguing sometimes never did no harm!" In that case did he have any theories as to who had killed him? "Yeah, look no further than that Claude. Mike had him on a yearly contract, and it's renewal time! Only it wasn't going to be renewed. Mike wasn't going to keep him—can't read his plans, it's just one untidy scrawl, and he's such a pompous ass!"

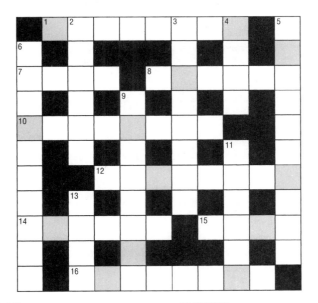

72

ACROSS

1 The sort of forest where Sam lives (8)
7 The great black dog's name (4)
8 The Russkie is a choice one (6)
10 Mike had recently made his workforce bigger (8)
12 It was a comical notion (8)
14 Where in Russia did Ivor come from (6)
15 Sam lives in a grotto (4)
16 Mike's creativeness had reached the zenith (8)

DOWN

2 Claude was on a yearly contract (6)
3 Mike lived in capitalist what (8)
4 Ivor had been rather this lately (4)
5 Sam stalks around wearing this (4, 6)
6 These were top secret (10)
9 Does Claude think he is Holmes's sidekick (2, 6)
11 His handwriting was untidy (6)
13 Mike wasn't going to retain him (4)

Dun Roaming

The body of Vera Weary has been found brutally strangled at the Tired Traveler Guest House. Superintendent U. Sless, being very tired, has fallen asleep in the lounge so once again it is up to you to catch the culprit.

MILES TOGO

"An utter tragedy!" groaned Miles. "Vera was an inspiration to all travelers—why, she was seriously off course in the desert in Australia but managed to find her way to Lake Frome using the Ursa Major constellation. She made a type of tepee out of animal skins and proved deft at catching the occasional lizard to eat. She was rescued by a Swede prospector. Her skin was burnt the color of ebony—she was lucky not to end up in the cemetery." Any clues who killed her? "I think it was Wendy. She's very jealous of Vera—her droll sense of humor, her contacts worldwide, everybody liked her!"

WENDY ROAM

"What iniquity!" exclaimed Wendy. "I had great respect for Vera. She's a celebrated explorer and author. When I was feeling off-color, she gave me an intriguing box she'd bought—it's a rectangle made of the wood of an apple tree, with an uneven pattern in brown carved around the edge." Any idea who killed her? "Rick—he hated her. When her poodle was barking the other day, he kicked it and she caught him and threatened to report him to the ASPCA!"

RICK SHAW

"What a crazy accusation," laughed Rick. "Under that woman's gorgeous brunette hair is an extremely obtuse mind! I also admired Vera—but not her dog! We had lots to discuss about her recently published biography of Anne Boleyn. I am a history teacher and I shall be setting an exam on the subject for my pupils." Did he know who had killed her, then? "I believe it was Miles. He'd asked her to dinner and when she ordered the most expensive meal, he didn't like what he had to spend on her!"

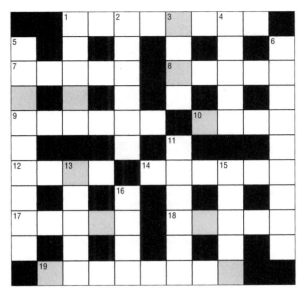

ACROSS

1 Vera's hair color (8)

7 The name of the lake (5)

8 The tree from which the wooden box was made (5)

9 Vera had to abandon her dinner with Miles (6)

10 She proved agile at catching lizards (4)

12 The constellation — Major (4)

14 The surname of the person the biography was about (6)

17 Miles had to shell out for Vera's dinner (5)

18 Her sense of humor (5)

19 She was lucky not to end up in a graveyard (8)

DOWN

1 The color of the pattern on the box (5)

2 The pattern was jagged (6)

3 Rick was going to set a test for his pupils (4)

4 The tent Vera made (5)

5 Wendy was seriously lost (3, 6)

6 The shape of the box (9)

11 What sort of dog Vera had (6)

13 What the prospector was (5)

15 The color Vera was burnt (5)

16 The box had the pattern around the rim (4)

74

Horseplay

The body of Slade Dinera has been found brutally murdered at the Happy Hunter Stables. As Superintendent U. Sless is absolutely terrified at the mere mention of the word horse, it is up to you to apprehend the culprit.

ORSON RYDER

"Well, well!" mused Orson. "Somebody finally bumped the Tsar off." Any idea who it was? "He and Di appeared to live in a state of everlasting hubble-bubble. She's such a dragon, they were always on the verge of eruption. She was furious when she found him having a siesta in the dell down by the river. A buyer had come to look at the Arab horses and she thought he was trying to hide, leaving her to do all the work!"

DI DINERA

"Nonsense!" exclaimed Di. "It might not be a marriage made in heaven but it was growing stronger by the year!" Who did she think had killed Slade? "That Des, who is a lazy so-and-so. His coffee breaks were like a piece of elastic—they were starting to elongate day by day! And his weight was going up and that agitates both myself and Slade—when the staff are too heavy for the horses! It doesn't take much to ignite our tempers!"

DES PARATE

"It wasn't me," whined Des. "It's not fair." Well, who was it then? "It was Orson—he's always remiss in his chores, sneaking off at the drop of a hat, claiming his throat is as dry as the Gobi, and must have a drink! What about mine, it gets parched as well! He says this place reminds him of the Orwell book—1984—with Slade and Di at the helm. There is always somebody watching and there is a definite tier of command—and he's at the bottom!"

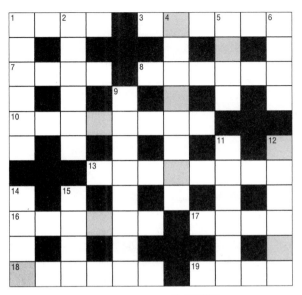

ACROSS

1 Di thought Slade was trying to conceal himself (4)

3 Des's bulk was going up (6)

7 What sort of horses were they (4)

8 They lived in a state of everlasting — bubble (6)

10 Des's coffee breaks were starting to increase day by day (8)

13 Slade and Di's marriage was growing better by the year (8)

16 Di was furious when she found Slade having a nap (6)

17 And what about —, it gets parched as well according to Des (4)

18 Orson was slack in his chores (6)

19 Slade was having his nap here (4)

DOWN

1 Their marriage was not made in Nirvana (6)

2 Di was a fire-breathing monster (6)

4 Always on the verge of this (8)

5 The desert Orson claimed his throat resembled (4)

6 There is a definite what of command (4)

9 It stirs up Di and Slade, when the staff are too heavy (8)

11 And it doesn't take much to start off their tempers (6)

12 The author's surname (6)

14 Orson's nickname for Slade (4)

15 Orson is reminded of *1984* with both Slade and Di at the wheel (4)

SOLUTIONS

1

Culprit:
Ina

Weapon:
teaspoon

	M	A	T	E	R	I	A	L		S
A		M			D		U		K
S	K	I	N		J	O	C	K	E	Y
P		D		I		L		E		S
I	N	S	O	M	N	I	A			C
R		T		B		Z		L		R
A		D	E	M	E	R	A	R	A
T		L		C		D		R		P
I	T	A	L	I	C		P	I	P	E
O		V		L				A		R
N		A	N	E	C	D	O	T	E	

	V	A	S	E	L	I	N	E	
M		I		U		E		U		S
O	R	L	O	N		W	I	D	O	W
R		L		D		D		G		I
B	E	A	K	E	R		N	E	W	S
I			R		N					S
D	I	A	Z		Z	E	P	H	Y	R
I		L		S		L		B		O
T	R	A	M	P		S	H	O	A	L
Y		M		A		O		M		L
	D	O	O	R	K	N	O	B	

2

Culprit:
Terry

Weapon:
ball

3

Culprit:
Lou

Weapon:
plank

4

Culprit:
Peter

Weapon:
needle

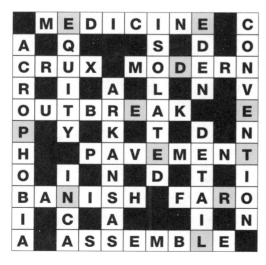

5

Culprit:
Frank

Weapon:
hoof pick

S	E	D	A	T	E			F	L	U	E
I		E				D		A			A
G	U	S	T		L	E	S	T	E	R	
N		P		D		F		E			W
	M	O	R	E	L	L	O				I
F		T		L		A		M			G
I			A	I	N	T	R	E	E		
N		B		G		E		X			K
G	A	U	C	H	O			F	I	R	E
E		R		T				C			P
R	I	N	K			A	C	C	O	S	T

G	A	S	H		T	U	R	N	I	P
E		O			N		A			I
N	O	R	A		S	E	N	I	L	E
I		R		O		A		L		R
A	L	O	E	V	E	R	A			
L		W		E		T		A		A
		A	R	C	H	I	V	E	S	
S		W		T		S		E		T
T	Y	R	I	A	N		O	R	F	E
O		I		K			S			R
P	O	T	T	E	R		T	E	R	N

6

Culprit:
Sol

Weapon:
hoe

7

Culprit:
Lena

Weapon:
hot coals

8

Culprit:
Lester

Weapon:
cue

9

Culprit:
Gary

Weapon:
rod

S	T	A	R	C	H		W	A	G	E
O		M			D		I			X
L	E	A	N		G	R	U	D	G	E
O		Z		B		I		E		M
	C	O	L	U	M	B	O			P
R		N		C		B		R		T
A			S	K	I	L	L	E	T	
F		L		E		E		B		T
F	E	I	S	T	Y		Q	U	A	Y
I		D		S				K		N
A	H	O	Y		A	D	H	E	R	E

R	E	E	D		K	E	E	G	A	N
U		X				V		R		I
S	L	O	G		T	A	X	I	N	G
T		T		C		P		T		H
I	R	I	S	H	S	E	A			
C		C		A		R		M		D
			C	R	E	O	S	O	T	E
A		E		I		N		N		L
M	E	D	U	S	A		L	A	C	E
M		I		M				C		T
O	U	T	L	A	W		L	O	S	E

10

Culprit:
Eric

Weapon:
cord

11

Culprit:
Helen

Weapon:
vase

12

Culprit:
Bertie

Weapon:
hoe

13

Culprit:
Ina

Weapon:
curtain

14

Culprit:
Sue

Weapon:
knife

15

Culprit:
Ed

Weapon:
glass

16

Culprit:
Coral

Weapon:
stiletto

17

Culprit:
Tom

Weapon:
wrench

S	A	M	O	S	A		E	L	A	L
E		A			S		E			A
M	I	N	I		F	I	N	E	S	T
I		U		S		B		R		V
	P	R	E	T	Z	E	L			I
A		E		R		R		M		A
S			C	O	M	I	C	A	L	
T		A		K		A		N		S
H	E	B	R	E	W		W	I	C	K
M		L		D				L		I
A	N	E	W		L	I	Z	A	R	D

18

Culprit:
Isa

Weapon:
rope

R	U	I	N		R	O	L	L	E	R
E		N			M		O			O
F	A	D	E		G	E	R	B	I	L
U		I		C		L		E		E
G	R	A	N	U	L	E	S			
E		N		L		T		F		G
			T	O	R	T	I	L	L	A
S		P		T		E		E		L
K	R	A	N	T	Z		V	E	A	L
I		I		E				C		O
P	E	R	U	S	E		Y	E	L	P

19

Culprit:
Pearl

Weapon:
wine

20

Culprit:
Tina

Weapon:
brush

21

Culprit:
Ben

Weapon:
tire

22

Culprit:
Claire

Weapon:
gun

23

Culprit:
Cleo

Weapon:
scissors

24

Culprit:
Matt

Weapon:
roller

25

Culprit:
Ben

Weapon:
whip

W	O	M	B	A	T		M	A	N	E
E		A			B		S		D
L	I	N	E		R	E	V	I	E	W
L		T		D		A		A		A
	A	L	B	E	R	T	A			R
P		E		F		R		F		D
U			L	U	C	I	F	E	R	
R		B		N		X		T		V
S	P	E	E	C	H		R	I	B	S
U		A		T			S		O
E	T	N	A		M	I	S	H	A	P

26

Culprit:
Arty

Weapon:
bust

D	E	S	K		R	A	M	B	L	E
E		E			C		L		L
D	O	N	E		A	C	C	E	S	S
U		I		R		O		W		E
C	L	O	V	E	L	L	Y		
T		R		S		A		C		S
		H	O	O	D	W	I	N	K
F		E		L		E		N		I
R	U	M	P	U	S		B	E	N	N
E		M		T			M		N
E	L	A	T	E	D		W	A	R	Y

27

Culprit:
Molly

Weapon:
pen

28

Culprit:
Evan

Weapon:
scalpel

29

Culprit:
Sam

Weapon:
rock

N	U	T	M	E	G			C	A	L	F
E		H					D		V		I
C	A	R	P			R	E	C	O	R	D
K		O		P		V		W			G
		O	N	T	A	R	I	O			E
C		G		L		A		A			T
A			L	A	T	T	I	C	E		
N		C		V		E		T			A
C	L	O	S	E	R			Q	U	A	D
E		M		R					A		U
R	U	B	Y			T	A	I	L	O	R

D	E	E	D			L	A	C	K	E	Y
A		N					P		E		A
L	U	D	O			V	E	N	E	E	R
L		E		S		R		E			N
A	N	A	L	Y	S	I	S				
S		R		N		T		F			I
			C	O	L	I	S	E	U	M	
S		C		P		F		D			P
C	L	U	M	S	Y			C	O	L	A
A		R		I				R			I
R	O	B	U	S	T		L	A	I	R	

30

Culprit:
Alice

Weapon:
pistol

31

Culprit:
Ewan

Weapon:
hairpin

32

Culprit:
Otto

Weapon:
birdseed

33

Culprit:
Les

Weapon:
rake

F	A	C	T	O	R			H	O	L	D
I		O			M		B			R
L	U	R	E		P	A	G	O	D	A
L		R		A		D		E		W
	G	A	L	L	E	O	N			E
R		L		T		N		E		R
A			R	E	M	N	A	N	T
N		H		R		A		R		D
S	H	E	K	E	L		P	I	L	E
O		S		D				C		E
M	I	S	S		A	R	T	H	U	R

34

Culprit:
Lex

Weapon:
twine

S	W	A	B		T	A	U	G	H	T
I		G			L		A			A
S	U	R	E		C	L	O	V	E	R
T		E		A		S		E		T
E	X	E	R	T	I	O	N		
R		D		L		U		M		I
			B	A	L	L	R	O	O	M
S		V		N		S		T		P
W	R	E	A	T	H		E	L	B	E
A		E		I				E		D
T	H	R	A	S	H		L	Y	L	E

35

Culprit:
May

Weapon:
crane

	J	U	R	A	S	S	I	C	
A		E		H		E		M		G
R	A	T	T	Y		N	E	P	A	L
I		T		T		T		E		A
S	C	Y	T	H	E		C	L	A	M
T			M		H					O
O	N	C	E		N	U	M	B	E	R
T		O		P		S		O		G
L	U	N	G	E		T	I	A	R	A
E		G		R		L		S		N
	M	O	N	U	M	E	N	T		

36

Culprit:
Bart

Weapon:
pot

T	O	P	G	U	N		O	V	A	L
Y		E				P		I		E
P	L	O	P		C	A	N	N	O	N
E		P		U		L		E		T
	C	L	A	T	T	E	R			I
G		E		T		T		A		L
R		N	E	A	T	E	S	T		
O		B		R		E		S		A
U	N	I	C	E	F		Z	I	N	C
N		A		D				S		H
D	U	S	K		C	L	A	I	R	E

37

Culprit:
Miles

Weapon:
tie

38

Culprit:
Al

Weapon:
anchor

39

Culprit:
Ed

Weapon:
bottle

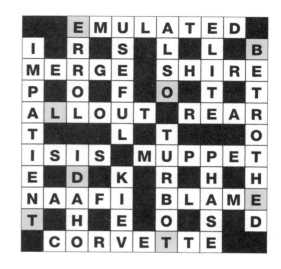

40

Culprit:
Sally

Weapon:
pot

41

Culprit:
Dai

Weapon:
harp

L	Y	R	E		H	O	N	E	S	T
I		O			L		C			A
F	L	A	B		B	I	S	H	O	P
F		C		I		V		O		E
E	N	H	A	N	C	E	D			
Y		E		S		O		J		D
			B	A	R	I	T	O	N	E
S		F		N		L		V		C
W	I	L	L	I	S		B	I	E	R
A		I		T				A		E
P	O	P	E	Y	E		G	L	U	E

42

Culprit:
Noel

Weapon:
tea towel

	U	T	E	N	S	I	L	S		D
A		A			N		O			O
F	U	S	S		A	S	Y	L	U	M
T		S		S		T		D		I
E	L	E	C	T	R	I	C			N
R		L		U		N		S		E
W			T	R	I	C	Y	C	L	E
A		S		G		T		A		R
R	O	T	T	E	N		B	R	I	E
D		U		O			C			D
S		D	E	N	T	U	R	E	S	

43

Culprit:
Chip

Weapon:
hook

44

Culprit:
Archie

Weapon:
axe

45

Culprit:
Stan

Weapon:
broom

46

Culprit:
Ian

Weapon:
vase

47

Culprit:
Tara

Weapon:
hat pin

48

Culprit:
May

Weapon:
sash

49

Culprit:
Theo

Weapon:
pencil

50

Culprit:
Syd

Weapon:
lamp

51

Culprit:
Avery

Weapon:
club

S	E	R	F		S	U	P	E	R	B
A		E			N		M			E
T	I	F	F		A	D	V	I	S	E
U		U		H		U		T		R
R	A	N	D	O	M	L	Y			
N		D		N		A		A		E
			F	O	R	T	K	N	O	X
A		A		L		E		K		C
M	U	S	E	U	M		M	A	C	E
I		T		L				R		E
S	L	I	P	U	P		B	A	R	D

52

Culprit:
Lottie

Weapon:
rake

	A	T	H	E	R	T	O	N		R
A		U			R		E			O
M	I	R	E		L	I	V	E	R	Y
Y		T		S		A		D		M
J	U	L	I	E	N	N	E			A
O		E		R		G		I		R
H			F	E	E	L	I	N	G	S
N		I		N		E		B		D
S	T	R	E	A	K		N	O	S	E
O		I		D				R		N
N		S	T	E	R	L	I	N	G	

53

Culprit:
Al

Weapon:
fuse wire

		F	E	S	T	I	V	A	L	
	S		R		A		T		C		G
	P	E	A	R	L		C	A	U	S	E
	E		M		A		H		T		L
	C	H	E	E	R	S		D	E	M	I
	U			Y		E					G
	L	E	S	S		O	X	Y	G	E	N
	A		T		A		P		R		I
	T	W	A	I	N		E	V	I	C	T
	E		R		T		R		L		E
		O	R	I	E	N	T	A	L	

54

Culprit:
Bea

Weapon:
putter

S	P	O	I	L	T		F	O	I	L
U		R			J		R		A
L	O	C	K		H	A	W	A	I	I
K		H		I		N		L		D
	K	I	N	G	P	I	N			O
H		D		N		T		D		N
O			S	O	L	O	M	O	N	
B		A		R		R		M		R
B	U	N	K	E	R		L	I	M	A
L		T		D				N		T
E	R	I	K		A	L	G	O	R	E

55

Culprit:
Ty

Weapon:
dagger

56

Culprit:
Lou

Weapon:
can opener

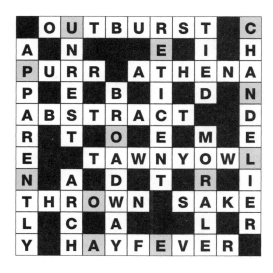

57

Culprit:
Phil

Weapon:
radio

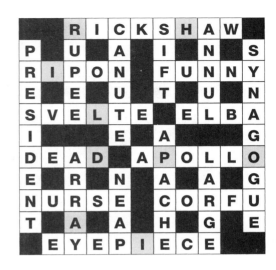

58

Culprit:
Noel

Weapon:
stylus

59

Culprit:
Al

Weapon:
chain

60

Culprit:
Walter

Weapon:
racket

61

Culprit:
Rosie

Weapon:
bottle

		S	Y	L	L	A	B	L	E	
A		I		O		P		O		S
L	O	T	T	O		S	K	I	R	T
L		A		F		E		R		U
B	U	R	E	A	U		H	E	A	T
L				H		M				T
A	K	I	N		M	O	R	O	S	E
C		B		M		S		R		R
K	N	I	F	E		Q	U	A	K	E
S		Z		S		U		T		D
	C	A	S	H	M	E	R	E		

C	I	R	C	L	E		B	I	K	E
A		O			M		N			Y
S	P	U	R		G	A	U	C	H	E
T		S		A		N		H		L
	B	E	R	M	U	D	A			E
F		D		A		E		H		T
A			S	T	I	L	T	O	N	
T		A		E		A		N		G
H	U	B	B	U	B		I	O	W	A
O		E		R				R		L
M	U	L	L		S	Q	U	A	L	L

62

Culprit:
Ina

Weapon:
cyanide

63

Culprit:
Bea

Weapon:
hacksaw

I	R	A	Q		C	U	C	K	O	O
M		N				M		W		X
B	A	N	D		A	B	L	A	Z	E
I		U		F		R		I		N
B	R	A	C	E	L	E	T			
E		L		A		L		E		C
			S	R	I	L	A	N	K	A
A		W		L		A		C		R
C	H	I	S	E	L		C	O	L	T
I		N		S				R		E
D	R	O	W	S	Y		H	E	A	R

	E	Y	E	L	I	N	E	R		I
E		O			U		E			N
R	E	N	O		C	R	U	N	C	H
I		D		O		T		T		A
C	L	E	A	R	C	U	T			B
T		R		N		R		B		I
H			F	A	C	E	L	I	F	T
E		O		M		D		S		A
R	U	G	G	E	D		F	E	R	N
E		R		N				C		T
D		E	S	T	I	M	A	T	E	

64

Culprit:
Clair

Weapon:
nail file

65

Culprit:
Nan

Weapon:
arsenic

Crossword 65 solution grid:

```
      O R C A D I A N
  S   L   O   I   R   D
  T W I R L   E A G E R
  U   V   L   T   U   C
  P R E V I N   Y E A R
  I     E   S       I
  D I O R   P H I L I P
  I   U   U   R   E   P
  T E N O R   I N A N E
  Y   C   G   M   R   N
    P E T E R P A N
```

66

Culprit:
Millie

Weapon:
pistol

Crossword 66 solution grid:

```
B O R D E R   F I L E
O   A     R   O     U
W A R M   S E C T O R
L   I   A   G   A   O
  S T I R R U P     P
H   Y   R   L   S   E
E     T I T A N I A
C   O   V   R   E   D
T O P H A T   X R A Y
I   A   L       R   E
C A L L   T A B A R D
```

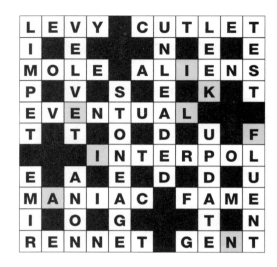

67

Culprit:
Ali

Weapon:
knife

L	E	V	Y		C	U	T	L	E	T
I		E			N		E			E
M	O	L	E		A	L	I	E	N	S
P		V		S		E		K		T
E	V	E	N	T	U	A	L			
T		T		O		D		U		F
			I	N	T	E	R	P	O	L
E		A		E		D		D		U
M	A	N	I	A	C		F	A	M	E
I		O		G				T		N
R	E	N	N	E	T		G	E	N	T

68

Culprit:
Les

Weapon:
peeler

	B	R	O	C	C	O	L	I		P
E		E			V		D			E
X	M	A	S		F	E	E	L	E	R
H		D		M		R		E		M
A	D	E	Q	U	A	T	E			I
U		R		T		I		U		S
S			S	E	G	M	E	N	T	S
T		F		S		E		T		I
I	N	L	A	W	S		E	R	G	O
V		O		A				U		N
E		P	E	N	N	I	N	E	S	

69

Culprit:
Daisy

Weapon:
venom

70

Culprit:
Ivor

Weapon:
mallet

71

Culprit:
Coco

Weapon:
apron

72

Culprit:
Ivor

Weapon:
slide rule

73

Culprit:
Wendy

Weapon:
scarf

Grid 73:

	B	R	U	N	E	T	T	E	
O		R		N		X		E		R
F	R	O	M	E		A	P	P	L	E
F		W		V		M		E		C
C	A	N	C	E	L		D	E	F	T
O			N		P				A
U	R	S	A		B	O	L	E	Y	N
R		W		E		O		B		G
S	P	E	N	D		D	R	O	L	L
E		D		G		L		N		E
	C	E	M	E	T	E	R	Y	

Grid 74:

H	I	D	E		W	E	I	G	H	T
E		R			R		O			I
A	R	A	B		H	U	B	B	L	E
V		G		A		P		I		R
E	L	O	N	G	A	T	E		
N		N		I		I		I		O
			S	T	R	O	N	G	E	R
T		H		A		N		N		W
S	I	E	S	T	A		M	I	N	E
A		L		E			T		L
R	E	M	I	S	S		D	E	L	L

74

Culprit:
Orson

Weapon:
pole